D1610860

33

33

With the Help of Thomas

9/248885

by

INGRID WOLF

ROBERT HALE · LONDON

ISBN 0 7091 8138 8

Robert Hale Limited
Clerkenwell House
Clerkenwell Green
London, EC1

Photoset by
Specialised Offset Services Ltd., Liverpool
Printed and bound in Great Britain by
Weatherby Woolnough, Wellingborough,
Northamptonshire

Contents

PART ONE

Ville sans Lumière

1

The worst moment of a disaster is not the moment it happens. Shock blots that out. Nor the time immediately afterwards. You're playing at being brave then, showing the world – so you think, carrying the flag. No, the worst moment comes when you realize that nobody is looking, that nobody really cares – and why, indeed, should they? And there it is, that disaster, with you, with all its consequences, and it is going to stay with you, with all its consequences, for good.

When I had finished trying to break down the door of the church on Montparnasse, bruising my fists – as if accusing God would have helped, when I had finished crying, lying awake at night, seeing endless streams of refugees trudging past the black windows of my little room, it was still there, the knowledge that Austria had gone, that I had lost my country ...

What it meant dawned on me only slowly.

My going to the American Embassy to enquire about emigrating to the States was my sister Felicity's idea. I had been living in a little room one floor below her flat, since I had come to Paris for 'a few months' in October, to do a research job for the magazine on which I had been working.

Jean, my brother-in-law ('un artiste peintre'), came with me to the Embassy. We asked the caretaker at the lodge where we should go. He was busy (chasing a mouse in his lodge, hammering away at the creature with the heel of his shoe), not able to give us an answer; we had to wait. I wanted to leave there and then, but Jean would not let me. He felt we had not yet carried out our task to Felicity's satisfaction.

We went to the room the porter had indicated. It was a big room, full of counters, full of people. The walls were covered with green tiles. Jean took one look at the tiles, clutched his belly, said that it looked like a swimming-pool and made him want to pee, and disappeared. I stood about and watched the worried, pleading faces in the queues, in front of the counters, thought about the questions of quotas and sponsors, and could not carry on. I felt as if my small hope for a new life in America was represented by the scurrying mouse, which the porter had bashed to a pulp with the heel of his shoe.

When Jean came back, we did not talk; we just silently turned around and went home. We felt we had done enough.

I had not woken up. I was trying to live the life I had lived in Paris before the *Anschluss*. I had not yet realized that I was not the same person.

I was no longer a visitor: I was a refugee. It takes a while to get accustomed to that. Where was I going to be a refugee? Britain was out: one had to have proven means of livelihood for an entry visa. The idea of going to the United States I had abandoned. I was going to be stuck in France.

Of course there was no money coming in now. The research-work I had been doing for the editor of my magazine in Vienna was no longer needed. It was important to earn money, and equally important to find a room in which I could live. My little room below Feli's flat was not meant to be lived in: the only source of heat was a paraffin stove which smelled; the only way to wash, a tiny basin with a cold-water tap. I was dependent on the flat upstairs.

There is no shortage of hotels on the Montparnasse, but not all of them are clean; not all of them take dogs – I had my Alsatian bitch, Tova, with me; not all of them are agreeable to live in; in some the noise of the plumbing never stops.

At odd moments in my turbulent life I have been lucky, and I was lucky then, though the hotel I found was an uninspiring place, just around the corner from Feli's flat, in the rue Jules Chaplain. An uninspiring street as well ...

Arriving there, I walked into a pale, black-haired, unhelpful male, who said he had nothing to do with the hotel, and nearly walked out again. He called Madame – even that he did reluctantly. Madame appeared, small, square, wiping her hands on her apron, compassion written all over her wrinkled face. Madame let rooms only by the month, and yes, Madame would have a room free in three days. Madame did not mind my dog. I was home.

The room was a front room, and she liked to be paid monthly in advance, so she said at the time. (I would not like to guess how many tenants owed Madame rent.) When I first moved in, I did not know the significance of a front room as opposed to a back room, I did not even know there were back rooms. Just looking at the place, with its narrow façade, you did not expect the large number of rooms, much less the fine differences between them!

It had thirty rooms, ten in front, ten at the back, ten across the courtyard. The front rooms had tiny bathrooms; the back rooms had kitchenettes and utilitarian wash-facilities; the ones across the courtyard were family rooms (I did not inspect those). My front room had a splendid view of the kitchen of a Russian restaurant, and at night the noise from the kitchen prevented sleep; the smells had direct access and became nauseating – I have never looked borscht in the face since.

I did not need the tiny bathroom; a kitchenette, however, would have been bliss. I paid Madame three months rent in advance – it was all the money I had. I lived with the Russian kitchen and waited. Soon I had a back room on the fifth floor and the precious possibility of cooking (mainly coffee and spaghetti).

Living in that hotel was like living in a hive of fates, each cell having its own traumatic destiny. Spanish refugees, German refugees, Persian students, night-club dancers from the Montparnasse, Communists, Fascists, all religions, all political convictions. The back rooms housed Spanish refugee families with numerous children, and the family life of prostitutes, their pimps, sometimes their children, always their dogs, never their clients. The noise was terrific. It broke out of the windows, mixed into an orgy of sound in the narrow courtyard, mounted up the walls and broke into the rooms again: radios, voices, yelling children, whining dogs, quarrelling pimps, the whole human symphony.

From my window on the top floor, I could see across the roofs into the sky. It was early spring. There was that spring sky that I used to love in Austria, where it had always seemed full of promise.

I did not love it then. It did not seem to hold any promise for me. In the evenings it turned red from the glare of the lights of the Montparnasse.

From my window I could look into the windows which gave onto the same courtyard. I could see their occupants go busily and unashamedly about their little lives, dressed or undressed, hair in curlers.

And I could see the pale, black-haired, unhelpful male, Monsieur Louis, in the courtyard, fussing around the two cages full of canaries which hung outside Madame's sitting-room window. They were Monsieur Louis's canaries, no doubt about that. They seemed the only thing Monsieur Louis cared for in this world. The place in which the cages hung caught whatever sun penetrated the yard; in the sunshine the birds would get lively, twitter and sing; and Monsieur Louis would look nearly happy for a few moments. In the evenings he took the cages indoors, and when it rained, he kept them in the sitting-room. He lived with Madame.

When I first moved up to the fifth floor, I found it difficult to think constructively – indeed, to think at all. Everything around me seemed to have nothing to do with me. I was on the fringe, looking on. I stood staring out of the window for hours on end. Sometimes I wondered why I bothered to go up and down five flights of stairs, why I did not simply jump out of that window, down to Monsieur Louis and his canaries, and make an end of it all?

I have no confidence in suicide. I do not think it is a way out.

I did not jump. The pretence of having some sort of choice seemed attractive at the time.

2

During the first weeks after the *Anschluss* Tova let me down. She would not eat spaghetti or French bread, or drink coffee. But that was what I lived on. Tova did not want to stay in the room on the fifth floor all day; she was not interested in the life of the people in the hotel. She wanted meat and walks. Tova did not know that she was a refugee now.

I used to buy offal for her in a little shop which sold nothing else. There was a girl in the shop, a very beautiful girl, who looked like Snow White and had her arms steeped in blood up to the elbows all day. No spark in her eyes, a dead-pan Snow White, almost obscene.

No money, no offal. Feli arrived unexpectedly one morning at the hotel, just when I was having a quarrel with Tova about her demands, and we were both upset. A quarrel with Tova seemed like the end of the world to me. I was sitting on the floor, holding Tova in my lap and crying copious tears all over her, when Feli stepped in.

She yelled at me to go out and find some work, to stop feeling sorry for myself. Yes, with or without a work-permit! She was right, of course. She gave me ten francs to buy food for Tova and a coffee in a coffee-house for myself. It would cheer me up to get out.

From then on she used to drop a ten-franc piece in my letter box at the hotel on her way to market – it was a lot of money at that time. And occasionally she brought butcher's scraps or bones for Tova.

I decided to get a move on. Through friends of friends I started my career in futile part-time jobs, and some months later a French *fonctionnaire* I knew surprisingly came to my rescue.

Long before the *Anschluss* I had joined a group of three Frenchmen who met twice daily in a café on the Montparnasse: a professor, the *fonctionnaire* and an artist. The latter, an engraver whom I had met through Jean, had introduced me to the others. Before Austria crashed, I used to join them regularly after lunch or in the evening for a coffee and a chat. After the Anschluss I did not meet them quite so often. One day the *fonctionnaire* suggested that I apply for a work-permit and give him the application. To my surprise, the application was granted.

I found an 'official' job with a small unit which produced a fashion paper, a lousy little rag, run off stencils, which sold to provincial tailors all over the world. My calling was to translate boring sub-titles and descriptions into German and English. Knots and fringes, bows and laces, satin and velvet, this cut and that one. I had not been interested in fashion before; now I began to loathe it. Dungarees for me for the rest of my days!

Monsieur le Patron lost on the horses most of the money he received from his international subscribers. He then drank himself stupid because he had money worries. His female underlings he lured into a backroom with wild promises of paying their wages but pinched their bottoms instead in an effort to appear charming. He was fat, middle-aged, coarse. If the 'charm' failed, he would yell: "*Vous n'allez pas me faire des histoires pour quelques sales billets?*" If that did not work either, and one continued to harass him, one did eventually get paid.

It was tiring at both ends, that job. Boring and bothersome. But it paid for Tova's food and some of mine. Most important, it paid the rent.

3

My little hotel in the rue Jules Chaplain became part of me,
Madame Mollet, '*la patronne*', a friend. I shared her worries
about Blanche, her maid, and those of other tenants about
Monsieur Louis, Madame's boyfriend. Tenants of the hotel
were divided into 'we' and 'them'. 'We', the non-Fascists,
were more numerous; 'they' seldom lived in hotels, for 'they'
were on the winning side at the time.

I had been there about three months when Madame came
up to my room, knocked on the door and, shy and worried,
asked me if I was well. Puzzled, I assured her that I was fine.
Why ... hmm ... had I not yet had any ... hmm ... visitors? I
explained to her why I was not in an abandoned mood, and
her compassion knew no bounds. Madame now considered
that she should be a friend to me and as such told me about
her problems, one of which was Blanche.

Blanche came from the Calvados, had red hair and freckles,
was about thirty years old, limped, one leg being shorter than
the other, and had been with Madame Mollet for a long while;
Madame herself came from Lille. The two of them kept the
hotel clean and the tenants satisfied, Madame with a smile
and Blanche with a grumble.

Yet Blanche had a dream which kept her soul smiling, even
if the smile did not reach her face. Blanche dreamed about
being buried in the robes of a nun. To that dream she devoted
her life.

Originally she had wanted to become a nun, but it seemed
that convents did not accept people who were poor, or people
who were disabled, certainly not people who were both. So
Blanche was not a nun, she was maid in a small hotel, but on
her days off, she went to the convent round the corner, taking

with her any present given to her, her wages and her tips; that, and the blameless life she led, made the convent promise to bury her in the robes of a nun, after her death, and pay for the funeral.

Every so often Madame Mollet would explode and spill her fury into my room. Then I would try to calm Madame, make her understand that nobody could ask for more than the promised fulfilment of a dream.

"They are taking advantage of the poor idiot," said Madame.

"It makes Blanche happy, Madame Mollet, what more can you ask for her?"

We had that abortive discussion about twice a week for a year and a half.

Monsieur Louis made Madame happy. It did not seem tactful to point out to her that in all our eyes he also was a waste of good intentions! Monsieur Louis was hurt when he had to answer the telephone or sort the letters of tenants, offended if you asked him to carry a parcel or case upstairs, furious if you mentioned a blown fuse or dripping tap. "Always working for nothing! – *C'est Madame la Patronne!*" Bribery did not get you far either; money was no compensation for his efforts!

He was Italian by birth. The tide of the First World War had swept him into France; he had taken on French nationality. He spent his days in Madame's sitting-room, listening to the radio or feeding, fussing and talking to the birds in the courtyard. Aperitifs and meals filled the rest of his day.

He was younger than Madame. It turned out later that, unbeknown to all of us, he had a soul. At the time we despised Monsieur Louis and were sorry for Madame, because we felt that she, like Blanche, had a dream, but that she, like Blanche, was much abused.

Not exciting, that picture of my life after the Anschluss, but I was able to save enough money to take a holiday that summer, hiking through Brittany with Ursel, a German girl who had a surplus of *ad hoc* jobs and passed some on to me. She had been longer than I at the struggle for survival. (Later

I joined my family at the Île au Moines, where they had rented a house. Friends of Feli, Hans and Helen, German refugees who came over from the States once a year, had also rented one.)

Brave little Ursel! She travelled through her daily life with a typewriter and a heap of romantic illusions. The typewriter – called 'Antoinette' – fed her body; the illusions fed her soul, and the porters of various hotels saw to it that body and soul were kept together. They can be nasty, these porters; they are certainly powerful; most of them had connections with the Sûreté Nationale! But they were good to Ursel.

Immediately after Hitler came to power, her parents had sent her to Paris. She was eighteen and came to the big, hard city from a secure, small-town, middle-class background. Paris is hard! Ursel shared a flat with her uncle – more of a worry than a support. He had a succession of 'doubtful' jobs, disappeared from time to time – into prison? On business trips? We never knew which. I never met him.

At regular intervals Ursel would be ordered to present herself at the Préfecture de la Seine. The questions at these interviews were always the same. "Why do you live in Paris?" Because she liked living in Paris. "What are you living on?" A business friend of her father was sending her money from Switzerland; her uncle supported her as well. She knew it was not true; the man at the Prefecture knew it was not true; but it satisfied the rules, and that, at the moment, sufficed. No one had ever heard of Hitler.

Ursel's parents had disappeared. She did not talk of them. A valiant figure, that little girl. Black hair, black eyes, a bunny face, a very straight body, swinging steps. She never complained, never spoke of the past. She worked as a secretary for visiting businessmen, all 'wonderful', romantic figures, much to be admired. In and out of metro and buses she went, with 'Antoinette', the typewriter, the length and breadth of Paris (and no, she did not get tired: she had done ballet training and had learned not to get tired). Sometimes a 'boss' would take her out in the evening, and then her romantic soul soared.

Ursel had discovered me on one of my lonely expeditions to

the Coupole. I think I held the swinging door of the café open
for her and the inevitable 'Antoinette'. That was enough. She
promptly became my friend, admirer, protector; her loyalty
knew no bounds. She introduced me to many people, among
them Sven, a Dutch painter and art-dealer, and my life took
on a new dimension.

Sven was middle-aged and florid but still good-looking – an
attractive, warm personality. From time to time he held
exhibitions in industrial cities, on which occasions I became
secretary and receptionist. I left the fashion-rag without
regret. I had reached saturation point! I still did the odd
translation, even acquiring the German rights for a French
book.

Ursel and I met most nights somewhere on the Boulevard,
at the Chinese restaurant if it was early, at the Coupole or
Dôme if it was past eating-time, never at a fixed hour, in a
fixed place, by previous arrangement – it was not necessary.
We knew where we would most likely be, and if one or the
other was not there – well, never mind, we would see each
other tomorrow.

I have known deeper friendships than that between Ursel
and myself, but I have not known stronger ones. We cared for
one another; we respected each other; we were mates,
comrades. We needed one another. I send my love and
greetings to the girl of many years ago.

It was lucky for me that I had Ursel and Sven, and others
who came and went. We were sailing into the Munich crisis
that autumn, and my precarious relationship with the three
Frenchmen went up in a cloud of smoke.

The *fontionnaire* got very het up. Here he was, a blameless
man of thirty, in danger of having to join the army, possibly as
a private! What did he have to do with Czechoslovakia? Why
did France have any pact with those eastern countries? Twice
daily he sat over his coffee or his *fine* and loudly condemned all
foreigners.

The professor was worse. He taught in a boy's secondary
school and tried to write learned books. There was no danger
of his being called up: he was a hunchback, *un bossu*. But his
comforts were in danger, and to that he took unkindly. In the
face of Munich he became a member of the 'Action Française',

ranted against Blum and regarded everything that was happening as the fault of Jews and foreigners.

The engraver retired out of life and into his art; he had had a strong tendency to do that all along.

So that was the end of my relationship with the three Frenchmen, which had lasted nearly a year.

In my sister's home feelings also ran high. Feli saw Germans at every door. When Jean said that France had the Maginot Line which no German would be able to pass, Feli laughed hollowly. She had a profound respect for German efficiency, and with some cause. The baby cried because of the raised voices, and Pia, the Austrian mother's help, declared that she had better go home. She was sad and upset by her own decision. We were all upset by it.

Then the Munich Agreement came, and we sat around stunned and sick at heart. Sven spouted lengthily forth. He had already 'signed on' – you could practically see him on his white horse, flag in hand, storming the Bastille; Ursel's uncle disappeared once again, and the first Czech refugees began dribbling in, many of them from Austria, where they had been safe up to now. Ernest was among them.

I came upon Ernest, unexpectedly, in a street in Paris. Warm, generous Ernest, my mentor and protector in Vienna; Ernest, who used to be pink and shiny, elegant from top to toe, the man who had surrounded me with inexhaustible love and patience. I had owed him a lot in Vienna; later I was to owe him more.

It is the unexpected blow below the belt which lays you out: I thought I would faint when I so suddenly saw Ernest in Paris, looking old, shabby and thin. He tried to avoid me by crossing to the other side of the road; that meant that he knew about himself. I had to run after him.

He said he was fine. He had lost weight because of his diabetes. Oh yes, he had plenty of contacts in Paris, loads of them, no worry at all. He might indeed have had some contacts; someone might have owed him some money somewhere for musical rights. I hoped so. There was no getting close to him. "Don't worry, Engerl. I'm all right, Engerl." I gave him my address, made him promise to keep in touch. I was still 'Engerl' to him. Some vague resemblance to

a seventeenth-century angel had given me the name. It hurt,
meeting Ernest like that; it felt like having a scab torn off a
wound, making it bleed again.

Compared with others, he was among the lucky ones. He
was not in a concentration camp. As a Czech he had no
difficulty with his *permit de séjour* in France. By the standards of
the time nothing much had happened to him. He had stopped
being a citizen and become a refugee, that was all!

So why did it hurt so much? Why does remembering that
sudden encounter still hurt? Because one's mind boggled,
refused to take all the horrors in? You heard about cattle-
trucks and concentration camps. You had endless nightmares
about refugees trudging through a world that did not want
them. You survived that knowledge and lived on. Then
suddenly you were face to face with someone you had known
well, to whom 'nothing much' had happened, who
nevertheless was now a wreck.

It did hurt, and it still does. You bury pain, but you bury it
alive, and it keeps on living.

After Munich the atmosphere in Paris changed. For the
refugees doubts were resolved in favour of bureaucracy, not
humanity! Officialdom divided us into different categories,
subjected us to different rules. Among ourselves we were still
one: the homeless. As we saw it, some of us were lucky, others
not.

I was among the lucky ones. I had permission to stay and
permission to work. There were the less lucky ones, with only
permission to stay. Then came those with a short breathing-
space, a '*refus de séjour*', the post-dated deportation order,
which allowed them a week, two weeks, sometimes a month –
still lucky, because at least the next twenty-four hours were
safe. At the bottom were those with an immediate deportation
order. Deportation to where? There was no answer to that.
The border? Some prison?

France was overrun with refugees, pouring over the
frontiers at night. Now the Czechs joined the throng. They
were allowed to 'stay anywhere in France but not in Paris'!
Paris was bursting at the seams. The prices in those hotels
which did not ask for papers rocketed beyond reach; the
Prefecture became an overcrowded meeting-place, where

refugees spent hours, days, humbly awaiting the decision as to
their fate.

Madame Mollet no longer had cause to complain of my
being alone in my room. It was inundated. During the day a
young couple from Austria, who had a front room, used the
kitchenette in their efforts to keep alive. We called them 'the
Sparrows', they sat so close together, hand in hand, twittering
to each other in low voices. They existed unhappily from one
extension of a deportation order to the next, having visas for
America and tickets for their ship but neither the money to
reach it – in Amsterdam – nor the visas necessary for Belgium
and Holland. I do not know why it had to be Amsterdam. One
did not ask questions.

At night it was this deportee or that one, sleeping on the
floor of my room, being passed along the line so the police
would not catch up with him and deportation thus delayed.
Or perhaps someone 'safe', with a post-dated '*refus de séjour*'
but no money for a bed. You were surrounded by people who
were condemned without trial, having committed no crime.
When you went to the Prefecture – and everyone had to go
there sooner or later, you felt as if you had stolen the silver
spoons and still had sufficient conscience to know that that
was wrong.

Two more 'regulars' had joined Sven, Ursel and me at the
Coupole or Dôme: Peter, an Austrian who had managed to
persuade his firm to transfer him to their Paris office, and
André, an Italian, near to taking his finals in Medicine.

And then Hitler decided to 'free' some more suppressed
people, the Slovaks this time. The world began to smell of war,
tension mounted – within my family as well. Feli's baby cried
a lot, not yet having overcome the departure of the Austrian
mother's help. Jean and Feli quarrelled about the Maginot
Line: Jean believed and Feli doubted. A gulf opened up
between them, between those who had been through the mill
and those who had not. Not yet!

In the midst of it all, spring came to Paris and dressed the
city as if for a feast. Another gorgeous spring. A travesty!

4

Summer 1939. When I tried to work in some sort of holiday for myself, my attempts misfired.

Hans and Helen arrived early that year. Helen was about ten weeks pregnant. She was not well and had to live quietly. Hans had signed on for a lecture tour in England; he was under contract to the Carnegie Institute in America and would have to return to the States in September.

I went to stay with Helen in Neuilly near Paris. Of course I kept my room at the hotel – it was much too precious to me and to others to let go, but Helen and I did make plans to take a flat together in the autumn. She wanted to have her baby in Paris.

We were well into August before I finished my last job. Paris was empty. Feli, Jean and their baby had gone to Provence. Ursel had left early for the seaside, having a job waiting for her in Vichy at the end of the month. André had gone to the south, Peter to Switzerland, Sven north to some of his wealthy friends. Now Helen was leaving with Hans for a fortnight.

I was to go to the Côte Basque, where I had taken on a summer job with a German businessman, then living near London, who wished to combine work and holiday surroundings.

I was to meet him at Bordeaux. He arrived a day and a half late. We drove down to the Côte Basque. For five days I typed and re-typed memos, contracts and letters in three languages. Then news of the Russo-German pact reached my employer, and we drove 700 kilometres back to Paris with just the occasional brief stop for Tova. My boss delivered us at the hotel, paid me for the full two weeks, thanked me for my company and wished me luck. He would strongly advise me to get out of Paris, he added.

As if I could!

Everyone now returned to Paris. Ursel had cancelled her job in Vichy; Sven arrived on Saturday; André was back as well, but not Peter. Helen wired that she and Hans would be returning from their holiday and leaving for America as soon as possible – could she stay in Feli's flat in the meantime, while they obtained a passage to America and got the necessary permits for Juergen, Hans' secretary, who was a German political refugee and had not yet obtained his first citizenship papers.

The French people seemed bewildered by the Russo-German pact. What did it mean? Did they not have a pact with Russia themselves? Information was sparse, understanding non-existent. The Maginot Line was handed around like a bromide. I began to hate the Maginot Line. To me it seemed like a sickness which affected the eyes of people and blinded them, a bribe by the devil.

General Mobilization was declared a few days later, on Friday, 1st September. The great buzz of discussion and argument everywhere stopped, and silence fell like a blanket over Paris. There was no excitement, no rebellion, no enthusiasm. It was as if everyone had been stripped bare of arguments and emotions.

I waited for news from Feli and Jean. It seemed to me that they were late returning.

We were sitting in the Dôme on the Sunday morning, Sven, Ursel, myself, others, waiting for Hitler's answer to the second ultimatum. There was nothing to wait for, we all knew that. Still, we were silent, we were waiting. Buses and cars rolled past on the Boulevard – our suspense was so intense, so absolute, we wondered how they could still move. It was a nice, bright day, I remember.

Watches seemed to have stopped, but hearts beat as loud as alarm clocks. When somewhere a church clock crashed into our silence, striking the three-quarter hour, it sounded like a cannon-shot. An epidemic of goose-pimples broke out, and one felt shamed by the treason of one's flesh. Sven interrupted the silence, started babbling again about offering his services – to the Défense Civile if they did not want him in the army. We were all eager volunteers for the Défense Civile. In between typing filmscripts and looking after Helen, I had taken a special driving-test that would enable me to drive ambulances. We told Sven to shut up. He did.

Eleven o'clock crept up in thunderous silence. And went. I think even the waiters stood still; if cars and buses still rolled along the Boulevard Montparnasse, we did not see them. Not Ursel. Not I. We were still together, the two of us, still mates. The others, it seemed, had already broken away, on their way to become strangers, *en route* towards a different destiny, created by their differing circumstances.

Then the radio boomed over the terrace, at eleven-fifteen. The ultimatum had expired. France and England had declared war on Germany.

We were living history. Some people find that exciting. We were not keen.

We sat in that café like dummies. On the surface nothing had changed, but nothing would ever be the same again. We were saying 'Goodbye', Ursel and I. Goodbye to our childhood and youth, their dreams, pains, hopes. Whatever we had expected for our twenties, this was not it. We were saying 'Goodbye' to ourselves. Everyone was saying 'Goodbye'. Silently. What had been was gone. What was in store one did not know – only that one would have to live it. Or die it?

We were still sitting there like dummies when André arrived in his little sports car. He was worried about his Italian passport, his parents in Egypt, a return visa to France if he joined them. He rushed off. He had brought my mind back from the infinite to the finite. I decided to go home to find out if there was any news from my family. I could not understand why I had not yet heard from them, for Jean had only five days after General Mobilization to join his regiment? There was a cable at home saying he would arrive by train Sunday lunchtime. Now! I just had time to rush to the station.

His train came. So did three others. Crowds poured out, but I could not see Jean anywhere. I began to cry. I do not know why I cried. An elderly lady put her arms around me; she said there would be more trains in the afternoon. I felt ashamed and went home to the hotel. There seemed to be nobody about. I went back to the Dôme, then to Feli's flat, then back again. I did not know what to do with myself. I was waiting for something to happen and knew it could not happen yet.

Daladier had spoken. They were playing the *Marsellaise* in the streets of Paris. In the silent streets, in the empty streets. To me it seemed as if every Frenchman had gone home to pack his bags and give a last kiss to his wife and family. But I could not find my family. There was no further news from them.

Helen and Hans were not in the flat, but I finally came across Ursel in the Dôme. We had been looking for each other, missing each other. Ursel was frightened. She anticipated that she would be one of the first women to be interned, if internment for women came, because of her uncle, because she had no work-permit and all her bright lies would now officially be unmasked. We agreed on a daily telephone-call, at nine o'clock every morning, to check up on each other. That call soon developed into a telephone round.

Ursel and I spent the first night of the war together in my small hotel-room. We stared into the sky, a beautiful summer sky full of stars, and waited for the first air-raid alert. The night was long. Towards morning all conversation died. The hotel was still; only from next door, the room in which the 'Sparrows' lived, came scrabbling sounds and muted voices.

The Sparrows were packing. We could hear them walking about, talking; we could hear Paula sobbing. At some point in the night I went into their room. 'Mr Sparrow' had stopped hoping for a legal solution to their problem and was going to cross the frontiers illegally and on foot. He had ceased twittering and become decisive. He fancied neither internment camp nor deportation, not even the honour of fighting for France, should such an honour be bestowed on him, he said. He knew all about crossing frontiers without papers and on foot!

Paula still clung to the hope that her family in Germany, her parents and five younger brothers and sisters, were alive. She did not know whether to try to find them or to follow her husband; she had not heard from her family for two years. Undoubtedly she realized that they could not be alive and just held on to the dream for one last desperate moment. Surely there was still hope? Five brothers and sisters ...

We trotted out all the arguments we could think of, then they went that same night, towards dawn, two thin, hungry young people, unhappy and hunted, with one suitcase each.

They made it! There are miracles, and they made it. I later heard through the refugee grapevine that they did get to America.

Feli and Jean drove home during Sunday night. Feli brushed any reference to the telegram announcing Jean's sole arrival by train on Sunday brusquely aside: "Nonsense, of course we would not separate at a moment like that." In any case, they would need the car; they were going to drive on the same day, north, to reach Jean's regiment on the Belgian border. She flatly refused to stay in Paris with the baby while there was still the smallest chance of being with Jean; it would be a week at least before his regiment moved, and they could have one more week together.

There was chaos in the flat. Helen had fled, in search of a hotel-room. Hans was in the bath. Jean was trying to find his uniform. The baby, Fiona, left unattended in her cot, was screaming her head off. Feli was rushing to and fro, distraught, trying to unpack and repack for herself and the child, and not achieving anything.

I stood in the hall of the flat and prayed that Hans would get out of the bath. It was ludicrous. No one could get washed; Feli was casting hostile glances at the locked bathroom door, as if the whole situation, war and all, had been caused by Hans and his bath. Why he hid in the bathroom, I did not know either. Was he frightened? Ashamed? There was Jean, trying to get into his uniform and leave for military service, while he, Hans, was trying to get out of it all and to America. He had no choice. Did he feel Feli's reproachful looks through the locked door.

His own task that day seemed frightening to him. He had different offices and officials to visit; he must queue up and wait, be charming and grateful, in his fight for Juergen's papers, permits and visas. Internment camp, deportation – or America, it all seemed balanced on a knife's edge for Juergen; and Hans, with or without cause, felt insecure for himself in the face of all these harassed officials, as if his first American papers might let him down, might be found wanting.

Suddenly Jean shouted at me from the studio to get ready. Ready for what? Feli cried: "Where are you going?" in an agonized voice, as if Jean were leaving her there and then for ever, and looked at me in sheer agony. I realized that everything was infinitely worse for her than for me. I had only myself to lose.

Hans made a sudden dash out of the bathroom and out of the flat. His departure eased the tension.

Jean dragged me to the nearest café, ordered some breakfast and wrote a letter 'to whom it may concern'. The letter stated that I was his sister-in-law and had been living with him and his family for two years, that I had no intention of harming France and would do everything in my power for the 'common cause'; that he was a French officer and '*Ancien Combatant, Croix de Guerre*', willing to guarantee my behaviour.

"It is all I can do for you at the moment," he said. "I can't do much for Feli and Fiona or myself either. When God asks me what I have done with my life," he added bitterly, "I will tell Him I fought in two wars and did a bit of painting in between."

That was my first bit of paper. I collected more bits of paper in due course. I am a firm believer in papers now. No papers, no rights, no good! Always take care of your papers!

We ran to the nearest Commissariat de Police and got Jean's signature certified. Jean saw the Commissionaire, told him about me and begged him to look after me; then we ran home.

Two hours later they were gone, Feli, Jean and Fiona. It would not matter if they broke down now, said Feli with sudden pride, Jean was in uniform, he could probably commandeer transport.

"As soon as I know anything, I will write."

Wherever you went, whatever you did, asleep or awake, the knowledge that war had been declared stayed with you. It ate into you like acid. Against this unshiftable background were the people you knew, running in various directions, trying to solve their own problems.

Sven kept storming the Préfecture de la Seine on a daily basis; he was determined to join a fighting unit. André queued up at the Egyptian Embassy for papers. Peter agitated from Switzerland: he wanted to come to France in order to fight against Germany – were we sure that this was not possible? We were sure!

Helen and Hans were struggling for Juergen's papers. The day came when both of them, Juergen and Hans, had to travel to the internment camp to get Juergen's exit-visa signed by the camp commandant. They left early in the morning and returned late at night. Juergen had his permit, but it was a victory which we were too tired to celebrate. Hans spoke about the Czechs whom he had met at the camp: they were making an almighty row about being interned, he said. I could well believe that – they had some cause! I wondered about Ernest.

The earliest boat-train on which Hans, Helen and Juergen could get a booking was due to leave one week later, at night. Hours early for their departure, we had supper at a restaurant opposite the station. The streets were blacked out, the station as well. We crept cautiously along the platform in the unaccustomed darkness, trying to find the right coach. Helen's hand, in mine, was cold. We did not speak. They found their coach, got into the train, looked out. I could hardly make out their faces in the dark. Now that they were likely to depart, they seemed to realize that I was being left behind. Helen murmured something about hating to leave me. She did, I knew. Hans and Juergen mumbled inanities about hoping to see me soon.

The train pulled out slowly. I wanted to run after it. I could not believe that they were really leaving me behind. I wanted to scream: "Don't leave me, please, don't leave me ...". I did not scream. I did not even cry.

That long train, taking Helen away, disappearing slowly into the night, seemed like a final black line sealing my recent past.

My present felt desolate.

5

Then I was down-graded from refugee to enemy alien.

During the first days of the war, when I had offered my services to the Civil Defence, I had been sent back. There were too many French girls to be dealt with, who had priority.

The day after Helen left, I returned. I was told that, as an Austrian, I was an enemy alien. As an enemy alien I could not be employed in the Civil Defence of France. I wrote to Jean and asked him to help. He wrote to a friend in the War Cabinet, who wrote back to say I should not 'push' it, I would only make myself suspect.

There is no bottom to the abyss into which one can be plunged. By fate, circumstances, one's fellow-humans! If one happens to catch on a ledge and succeed in pulling oneself out of it, it is luck, sheer luck. Right and wrong, justice and injustice, are road-signs, which disappear once one goes over the edge.

You are lucky if you escape physical hardship – from hunger and cold to the unbearable. You are lucky if you manage to keep your self-respect. Or some of it!

That 'luck' leaves you with an unrepayable debt to those who were not 'lucky', who died, while you did not; survived, while you were not tested.

It leaves you with a feeling of guilt because you did not suffer as much as they did, and self-doubt, the not knowing how quickly you would have crumbled, how shamefully you might have given in.

That load: debt, guilt and doubt, you carry to the end of your days. You owe! And you remain afraid, because you do not know when your debt will be called in.

I found a note from Ernest when I returned to the hotel from the Civil Defence Centre. He would be waiting for me in the Coupole till five.

He looked better than when I had last seen him. He had not been to internment camp, though many of the later Czech arrivals had. Recently most of them had been released, for a Czech legion was being formed since Czechs had been classified as 'friendly aliens' and as such were allowed to fight against the Germans. There was a Czech Club now, to which he belonged – I had not known in Vienna that Ernest was Czech. He was too old for the Legion, he said, but might get some work connected with it.

I told him about my futile endeavours, my new classification and its probable consequence. I told him about the well-laid plans Ursel and I had made for our time in internment camp, the lessons we would give and arrange to receive, the physical exercises we would keep up. He was appalled.

"We can't have that, Engerl," he said seriously, as if he could prevent it, and ordered two more coffees as an immediate first step. "Pity that I can't marry you ..."

How was his wife? He had not heard, he said. In Germany they had killed mental-hospital patients.

"You must marry a Czech, Engerl," he said full of enthusiasm at his bright idea, "then you'll be a friendly alien. A 'white' marriage, you know. I'll see what I can do. I'll give you a ring."

I told him that I could not stay on in the hotel but would move into Feli's flat. There was no work now, no money for rent. I was glad that he looked better and behaved more like his old self, glad that he indulged once again in bright ideas and schemes, which seldom stayed with him beyond the point of invention.

I was not keen to leave the hotel, where everything spelled 'friend', was familiar, a support – even the noise from the courtyard, the quarrels of pimps with their girls, the crying children and whining dogs.

I was not keen to give Madame Mollet notice at that moment either. Many of her rooms were now empty.

We had one small tragedy before I left.

Monsieur Louis had been called up. He was a Frenchman now and had to do his duty.

He did not rant against it, as the *fonctionnaire* had done. He became very quiet, even paler, very sad, and stopped going for his apéritif. Nor did he complain about mealtimes any longer. He helped Madame Mollet to store in the hotel cellars the possessions of tenants who had fled or been arrested – a task Madame Mollet had inflicted on herself unasked, because "they might need their stuff, poor things". He was depressed and dignified about it. We became concerned about Monsieur Louis's new image.

At the last moment, on the day of his actual departure, Monsieur Louis and Madame Mollet got married. Perhaps they had not been able to get it fixed up earlier.

Monsieur Louis was already in uniform, he was a '*poilu*'. He looked like nothing on earth in his heavy gear; it practically swallowed him up. Sad eyes in a pale face, black hair and a lot of greycoat.

They came back from church flushed with excitement, furious with the priest who had mumbled about "living in sin and seeing the light at last". What sin, Madame Mollet wanted to know, how could love be sin? They invited some of their tenants for a glass of champagne, at about lunchtime. We said goodbye to Monsieur Louis then, for he had to leave in the early afternoon.

Towards evening Madame Mollet went into the courtyard to fetch the canary cages. I was packing in my room when I heard her scream. I looked out of the window and saw Madame crumpled up on the paving stones, just below the bird cages. I flew down five flights of stairs.

Blanche was already there; between us we half dragged, half carried, the incoherent woman indoors and put her on her bed. Then I went back to the cages.

They were all dead, the canaries, the little yellow birds. Nearly twenty of them, lying with their necks broken, at the bottom of the two big cages.

It must have taken the *poilu*, Monsieur Louis, quite a while.

It was lonely in Feli's flat, frighteningly silent. I slept in the

baby's room, all sky-blue. The room – so painfully bright –
was too still. In the studio the paintings had their faces to the
wall, and the easels stood bare. The empty flat echoed with
Feli's unquiet.

My livelihood now depended on English lessons I gave to a
naturalized Frenchman, a disagreeable, fifty-year-old Pole;
my security on the *concierge*, a large, good-hearted woman,
interviewed twice weekly by the Sécurité. Ursel and I
whispered in corners of small restaurants or cafés; she would
not come up to the flat, she thought it might endanger me.

One morning Ursel was gone.

The shock when there was no answer to my morning call
knocked the ground from under my feet. I could not believe
that it had really happened. I rang and rang; I made a
thousand excuses to myself: the telephone was out of order;
she had had to go out and would be back any minute.

In the end I did the one thing I had promised not to do, took
a taxi and rushed over to her flat. Too bad if it was under
surveillance, if I was arrested on the spot.

The police had come for her at six in the morning, said the
concierge, shrugging her shoulders and shuffling back into her
lodge.

When the police came for me some days later, I behaved
like an idiot. However much you prepare yourself, however
much you think you are ready to face events, when they
happen, you are taken by surprise. The knock came at seven
o'clock. When I opened the door and saw the police officer,
the shock went through me like an electric current.

He showed me his warrant and asked me to get dressed and
to accompany him to the station. He said nothing about
'packing a bag and taking two blankets', the ominous phrase
we had been warned about. I thought it might be for an
interview only.

I dressed well rather than warmly. I took high-heeled shoes,
instead of practical ones. I wanted to make a good impression,
look my best. The man stood in the room while I dressed; he
came with me to the bathroom, while I washed and brushed
my teeth.

When I had finished dressing, he told me to pack a bag and
take two blankets. I was in despair. I had all the wrong clothes

on, unsuitable for camp. Worst of all were the shoes. I did not know what to do, ask him to wait while I got changed or leave it as it was. In the end I toddled away in the high-heeled shoes, handing Tova over to Madame Davasze, the *concierge*. She was to let my family know.

The police-station was crammed with people, mostly men; there were only four women there, myself included. Everyone silent, everyone deathly pale, sitting on benches, pushing close together to make room for the next one. I took my place among them, and we waited. It was eight o'clock by then. Policemen were coming and going; they were rapidly moving about on stage. We sat motionless; we were background. One man in civilian clothes was sitting behind a big table in the room; he also was on stage. Time ticked away while we waited suspended.

Every hour or so the man behind the big table would shout: "Now, where are those damn papers? Why don't they come along? Ring up the Préfecture." One of the policemen would ring up the Préfecture and report that the papers were on their way. Every so often the man behind the table would turn around, look at us, shrug his shoulders and say: "I'm sorry to keep you all waiting, but I can't help it." And we would smile, subdued, ingratiating, grateful for these crumbs of politeness.

We all grew old in those endless hours.

At last the papers arrived. Man after man was called to the table, checked against his papers, told to sit down again. Finally it came to us four women.

The man behind the table looked at the papers, looked at the first woman, called the next, and the next, and the last one, looked at the papers again.

"I am so sorry," he said, "You have been brought here by mistake. *Une erreur!* They mistook your Christian names for those of men. You can go. *Vous êtes libre!*"

The men, who had been told to sit down again and continue to wait, rose like one, poured over us, held on to our hands, our arms, our shoulders, our clothes. They acted as if we were the last women they would ever see in their lives; they wanted us to take messages home to their wives, girl-friends, mothers, children, tell them this, tell them that. Suddenly we four were the mothers, the sweethearts, the wives, of perhaps thirty men.

We cried; all of us cried.

Then the police ordered the men away. We went out and were free. For a little while longer.

Tova greeted me enthusiastically on my return, and Madame Davasze gave me an unexpected, motherly hug, which made cracks in the thin veneer of my self-control.

We went to the Coupole later, Tova and I. We sat on the terrace and watched the world go by. It seemed to me that I was seeing everything with completely new eyes, that it was still a wonderful, wonderful world at moments.

What price freedom? It is priceless!

A card from Ursel came a few days later. It said that she was all right, to pack warm clothes and medicines. That meant that it was cold at the camp and that there was no doctor.

I had great faith in Ursel. Given half a chance, she would come through. She had courage and stamina and was adaptable, and the power of her rose-tinted illusions was behind her.

It was the 'why' that bothered me, the unanswerable why.

I would have given a lot to be able to see her again swinging into the Dôme or the Coupole of an evening, straight-backed and keen, only very slightly pulled down by the weight of 'Antoinette'.

6

A few days after my first 'round-up', Ernest rang. The telephone bell set my nerves jangling. Since Ursel's disappearance the flat had been as still as a morgue.

Ernest rang in the middle of a five to six p.m. English lesson, to the huffy disgust of my pupil, the Pole, who suffered from the illusion that he owned me, for the price of a lesson a day.

Ernest sounded urgent. Could he come round? Not till after six? All right, sixty-thirty then. He would bring a friend. "See you."

What friend, I wondered. I was not aware that he had friends in Paris.

I finished my lesson on the dot, pushed the reluctant Pole out, buzzed around the place at speed. I was excited. It seemed marvellous to have people come to see me. I lit a fire in Feli's best room, hoovered, dusted, dressed up, made up. The front-door bell rang at six-thirty precisely. Ernest and his 'friend' stood on the landing. I took no notice of the friend, I was too shocked at the sight of Ernest. He looked white, drawn. Was it the light of the staircase that made him look so pale?

I tried to take their coats, usher them into the sitting-room. The stranger obediently took his coat off and walked in – not Ernest. He firmly closed the door after his 'friend', refused to take off his coat, stood in the hall, collar turned up, hands rammed into his coat pockets. He suddenly seemed very tall.

"There you are, Engerl," he whispered, attempted a smile and gave the attempt up at once. "No, thank you, I don't want to stay. You get on with it. He is a decent chap, solid, you know, honourable. I met him at the Czech Club. He has volunteered for the Czech Legion. He'll be an officer. You'll be all right with him."

Out of his coat pockets came his hands, and his arms went around me.

"Take care of yourself, my Engerl. No harm must come to you."

A big hug. He swung around and was gone. I heard him go downstairs. I was torn between running after him and politely joining the stranger in the sitting-room, but remained rooted to the spot, paralysed by the sudden turn of events. I had not given Ernest's bright idea in the coffee-house another thought. Such things happen in novels, not in real life. They never happen to oneself.

Then I heard the house-door slam and knew that it was too late to run after Ernest. He had gone.

I stood in the hall, confused, my heart banging away the seconds. After a while I reluctantly opened the door to the sitting-room.

The stranger stood in front of the fire, his back towards me, his hands held out to the flames. He turned around when I came in, and I noticed that he had good hands. I found that reassuring but realized that I was afraid – afraid of an unknown man, who need not mean anything to me?

Afraid? Only fools are perpetually brave. Values had changed since Hitler came on the scene, since the war started – one's own value most of all. One had become jetsam, rightless, fair game. It was difficult to retain one's self-respect, but that was all that was left.

And it was autumn, a miserable autumn, cold and wet. Claustrophobia had started; the flat was becoming a trap. There was nowhere to go to, a bit of shopping, a dash in the Jardin du Luxembourg for Tova? During the day coffee-houses were raided; at night they were full of men in uniform. I had to stay away from those, for sitting next to one by chance was sufficient to be suspected as a spy.

I was afraid. Anything new, any further change, frightened me. What additional burden would this meeting lead to, what new problem? What was going to happen next? How

insulting, how demeaning would it be? I realized that I was on
the defensive before I had even looked at the man. I tried to
look up, to smile. I had the feeling that I was breaking my jaw
and looked away again quickly, before he could spot me
looking at him.

He was quite tall. He had fair hair, receding from his
forehead, long at the back, untidy hair. He held one hand out
to me, mumbled something I did not catch – the noise in my
ear drowned all other sound – shook hands, gave me a
lop-sided smile. It was a nice smile. I noticed that he had blue
eyes and a generous mouth, that he pulled one shoulder
higher than the other and stooped slightly.

I turned two easy chairs towards the fire, bade him sit
down. We sat down. The stranger was perching at the edge of
his chair; his hands were on his lap; he kept clasping and
unclasping them. I found that reassuring as well.

The silence was terrific, unbearably loud. I had to do
something. I put more wood on the fire. It was unnecessary. I
curled up in my chair and waited. The flames in the grate shot
up, high and bright. I immediately worried that I might have
caused a chimney fire in Feli's best room. You do hang your
fears on the most idiotic hooks!

The stranger cleared his throat. He cleared his throat a
second time. He gave a kind of gasp and said:

"My name is Deichsler. *Ingenieur* Deichsler. I come from
Brno. My father was stationmaster in Brno."

He stopped. The fire was making a noise, but apart from
that, it seemed still in the room. It was not still – the rain kept
drumming on the window panes. Life was holding its breath.

I have often wondered why that simple statement made
such a deep impression on me: "My father was stationmaster
in Brno."

The words took away the edge of my terrors. They belonged
to another age, to fairyland: once upon a time ... lived happily
ever after ...

A miracle had happened. Oh yes, they do occur, small
redeeming miracles in the midst of vast upheavals – flowers
among ruins. That the Sparrows, so young and unable,
reached America was one. What happened to me was another.

Whosoever escaped, undestroyed, had lived a miracle.

And if it had been a different stranger who came along?

I cannot imagine, and I tremble to think what would have happened to me if it had been a different stranger who came along.

7

The stillness was even greater after the stranger had spoken. Outside, it was quite dark. Curtains had had to be drawn, muffling the noise of the rain. Inside, a standard-lamp threw a circle of light behind us, and the dancing flames reflected on our faces.

We were sitting in front of the fire, the stranger and I, staring into it, careful not to look at one another. I had been listening to the noise of rain and wind and the fire, when the stranger's voice had broken in, saying:

"My name is Deichsler, *Ingenieur* Deichsler. I come from Brno. My father was stationmaster in Brno." He had said it as if he were reading it from a script.

The words hung in the air like lanterns. They became lonely in the silence that followed. I tried to say something, make a sound. No! My body seemed frozen into the chair in curled immobility. My head was filled with the noise of an express train rushing me too fast through a night. I could not wrench a single thought out of it.

"His name was Leopold. His friends called him Poldi. He worked overtime on Saturdays, extra shifts, so that he could take us out on Sundays," the stranger continued, "when we were little, my brother and I. Later, when we were bigger, he worked extra shifts Saturdays and Sundays to put my brother through college. My brother is older than I, five years older. His name is Erik." He was still speaking in that low monotonous voice, but now he suddenly said in a different, lively sort of tone: "My grandfather had an open fire like this in his house."

He spoke with pride of his grandfather. He had owned some land. He had been a fantastic man, strong, full of energy, with a big appetite and a terrible temper. He had been a craftsman who built farm-wagons, that was where their name came from: Deichsler. "I spent my holidays with him as a child.

"My father was gentle," the stranger continued. "He spent a lot of time with me. Erik was Mother's great support." He stopped in his recital.

I looked up. I saw that he was no longer looking into the fire: he was looking at his clasped hands. I noticed that the knuckles of his fingers showed white.

The elder brother had stayed behind with their mother, he went on again while he himself had come over to France. "In January '39, I was hoping to gain a foothold in France and bring them both out." He had brought various patents with him.

"Engineering patents," he explained. "Erik qualified as an engineer just before the last war, in 1914. They put him on to war work." He was looking up from his hands, staring into the fire again. I was wondering what had happened to him in the First World War, and as if he had heard my unspoken question, he said: "I joined in 1915 as a one-year volunteer. I was seventeen." He sounded sad.

It was a strange sort of sadness. It seemed to settle first on this unknown man, to envelop him like a cloak, then it spread over me. I could feel myself being drawn into it, a vortex of despondency. I wondered what was happening. The express train stopped rushing me quite so fast through a night; my body unfroze. I was able to uncurl, sit up. I found my voice, was able to ask what had happened. .

"I suppose I played up," said the stranger. "I probably wanted to be a hero, not the lowest form of life, ordered about, yelled at. A one-year volunteer at seventeen – it made me a hero in my own eyes. Perhaps I hit on an anti-semitic officer ... I don't know." There was no reproach in his voice. The way he spoke reminded me of the people in Dostoevsky's books, with their patient acceptance of good and bad. "I went from punishment to punishment. In the end I got stuck on the Isonzo front for months on end without leave. Then they shipped me home with various medals, shell-shock, heart-trouble.

"Well, that's it, really." We were back to the script-reading again. "Father died in 1919. Erik saw me through college. I worked for many years in sawmills in the Carpathian woods. Later Erik took me into the small firm he had built up. Factory installations. We worked for Skoda among others."

As if in a nightmare, I was trying to break through my silence, say something adequate, reassuring, something that might penetrate the immense sadness that had settled on the man. I did not find the right words. I said:

"It is very nice of you to tell me about your family and yourself. You really don't have to."

I was immediately ashamed. I had meant to express appreciation for the respectful way in which he had behaved, had avoided abusing the situation.

There was a long pause after my terrible remark. The stranger was slowly drawing himself up until he was sitting straight and upright in his chair. He had unclasped his hands. I was looking at him but he was not looking at me.

"I am not out for adventure," he said in an off-hand voice. "Nor – I believe – are you? I understood from Ernest that you need help?

"I do not know Ernest very well. Only from the Czech Club. He sought me out. He sounded me out! He told me a lot about you, your parents, your background. I thought it only fair that you should know something about me.

"Well, there it is. I have signed on for the Czech Legion. We are waiting for official French Government approval. It has been promised and should come soon now. Once we have received that, I will have to join my regiment, in a week to ten days' time. I should have my old rank back, First Lieutenant. I was married in Czechoslovakia, but I'm divorced. We divorced by common consent. I have a little girl."

The sadness gripped him again. I could feel it. It was so strong I expected to see it surrounding him like a cloud. He got up, wandered about, studied Jean's paintings on the wall. He still did not look at me.

"If you like," he said, "we could go through some official form of marriage ceremony at a registry office. As the wife of an Allied officer you would be safe from internment camp. Then at a convenient date we could apply for divorce – it is quite easy to get a divorce for a war-time marriage. If I survive! There is certainly no reason for you to be afraid of me," he added, sounding stiff and pompous.

When the blue-eyed stranger did finally turn around, and our eyes met for the first time, I could feel myself grow small and ugly with shame. His need was in his eyes, pain, loneliness, hurt. Generously he had been offering me help: his nationality, his rank, his trust. Had he hoped for comradeship, friendship?

He must have been hurt by my cool reception. He must have thought me insensitive, arrogant. I had been concerned only with myself, my fears, my suspicions.

With great effort I asked him what his Christian name was, and he said:

"Edmund. *Ingenieur* Edmund Deichsler from Brno." He made a stiff little bow. "My friends call me Eddie," he added.

I asked him if he would like a cup of coffee.

"No, thank you. I will have to go now."

Eddie Deichsler, engineer from Brno, had had enough of his visit to a maiden in distress. He looked exhausted. His eyes left mine; he was walking towards the door.

"I must go back to the club now, they are expecting me," he said. "I will try to find out there what has to be done to get a marriage through in a week or ten days. I'll be back tomorrow, after lunch, at about two." He left.

I stood bereft. I did not think that I would ever see Eddie Deichsler from Brno again. I stared blankly at the door of Feli's room, which he had so silently and firmly closed behind him. He had tried to show me a way out of the trap, and I had slammed the door in his face. He had held out a hand in friendship, and I had not taken it. What I had feared most had come true. I had lost judgement, could no longer rely on myself. I had become a mean little heap of suspicion and fear and let us all down, the stranger, Ernest, myself.

I crawled around the place the next morning, unable to settle to anything, trying to prepare Boulonski's lesson, correcting his homework, watching the clock — one of those creeping, unending mornings.

Eddie appeared punctually at 2 p.m. He rang the bell and stood in front of the door, a bright smile on his face, a bunch of violets in his hands, and said that we would have to go to the

Czech Legation. Now! I took my coat, obediently trotting behind him down the stairs, with no thought about my pupil arriving at five.

I was filled with joy at Eddie's return. I thought those violets the most precious flowers on earth. And thus, light-heartedly, armed with a bunch of flowers, we entered the Paper War. The battle for documents was on!

8

We lost the first rounds, but till the last evening together it did not seem to matter.

To get a marriage through under our circumstances at that moment bordered on the impossible. One alien without papers, the other suspect! Eddie needed his birth-certificate and legal proof of his divorce. He had only his passport; his papers were in Brno.

We travelled backwards and forwards between embassies, ministries, military authorities, police authorities, legations. We sat long hours in waiting-rooms, sometimes forgetting what we had come for, we were so busy getting to know each other. We had little money between us, so we calculated fares down to the last centime and squeezed cups of coffee out of our knife-edged calculations. In the evenings I prepared food in the flat. I had introduced Eddie as my 'fiancé' to Madame Davasze, so the Sécurité Nationale could be informed; Eddie left the house at 9 p.m. sharp.

We went along the path of difficulties and frustrations filled with the deep warm joy of not being one alone any more, but two together.

Towards the end of the first week we were told that the Czech Military Authorities might give 'dispensation' to their fighting men: "... duplicate papers might be issued based on available information supported by two witnesses ...". When? "As soon as we have official permission to form the Legion. Come back tomorrow." The search for witnesses began next day, but they were not easy to trace. Official addresses of small hotels around Paris were meaningless, and unofficial bolt-holes in Paris changed nightly, and not everyone in the

Czech Club knew Eddie from Brno. By the time we reached
Army headquarters with the names of two witnesses, Eddie's
CO had left for Agde, where the regiment would be stationed.

Time had run out on us. The tomorrow of Agde, which we
had tried to ignore, came; our nine-day world was reaching its
end.

On the last evening we sat bereft of speech because now
there was nothing more to say.

"Three weeks," mumbled Eddie into one of the many
silences. "It shouldn't take longer to get duplicate papers.
Then I'll ask for compassionate leave."

It surprised me that he thought they would still be in the
South of France in three weeks time.

"It will take time to turn us into a fighting unit. There are
so many middle-aged professionals among us."

His lop-sided smile hurt. "Even if I do get my papers, they
might not give me leave. The CO might insist that I get
married in Agde."

"I'll come to Agde if need be."

There was that silence in the room again – the loud silence
of the first afternoon. Rain beating against the windows, the
fire crackling in the grate. I had made a decision. A welcome
decision? I did not know. I added hastily: "If you want me
to ..."

Eddie repeated: "If I want you to?" with such astonishment
in his voice that my confidence collapsed.

"Sure. If you want me to."

"You mean – to stay? For real?"

Slowly we came to the conclusion that it was to stay and
was for real. Eddie started to explain with great pomposity,
that he had nothing to offer me, no money apart from his pay,
possible physical hardship, no certain future. I told him that I
had had excellent training in camping. Anything to cut
through the tense atmosphere.

We lived a moment of intense happiness. We were giggly,
like children at a party. Eddie walked about murmuring "For
better or for worse", as if they were magic words. We drank a
toast to ourselves.

"If we are still together after the war," Eddie said, when we had calmed down a bit, "and it is not possible to return to Czechoslovakia, we could try to get to Canada. I should be able to get a job there with my experience of sawmills. We could live in a log cabin in the woods."

The light-hearted statement threw me! This was a new dimension altogether. In all the weeks since the war began, the idea that one day it would end had never entered my head.

I sat stunned after Eddie's invention of a possible future, stared at him. And suddenly I did not see him. A picture had flashed into my mind. I saw it very clearly then. I remember it very clearly now. A picture-postcard sort of picture of a log-cabin in a small clearing in the middle of a wood, high pine trees, a brook running at the bottom of the clearing. I cannot see the brook, but I know it is there. I am sitting in the kitchen of the log cabin, a large farm-house kitchen. I can see outside and inside simultaneously. I am sitting next to a well-scrubbed wooden table and stirring something in a huge pot. I am not looking at what I am doing. I am looking at the door.

The door leading to a paddock is open. A boy stands in the open door. There are other children behind him, I know, but these I cannot see.

The boy is between six and seven years old and bright with life. He is sunburned. He has bare feet and brown legs, and wears coloured shorts and an open yellow shirt. He has huge shining dark eyes and fair tousled hair. He holds the doorknob in his hand. I know that he is hungry. He has come in for his supper. He is happy. He is smiling at me.

His name is Thomas. He is my son.

The log cabin in the woods and Thomas. I looked at my dream for a long time. It seemed to me that the world had just been re-invented for me.

Eddie must have been perturbed by my long silence.

"We don't have to go to Canada," he said. "It was just an idea." Oh, but I did want to go. I told him so.

"There should be a brook at the bottom of the clearing."

He added a hot spring to the brook. We spun the dream out for the rest of the evening. I did not tell him about Thomas.

That evening Eddie stayed till after eleven. As soon as he had left, I was afraid again.

A friend of his rang next morning. He had seen Eddie to the

station. A first-class coach had been put on the train for the officers going to Agde. Eddie sent his love.

A card arrived a couple of days later, saying that he had arrived safely.

Then I heard nothing for weeks.

9

The weeks following Eddie's departure were the worst of this whole dreadful period, for the days I had had with him were wiped off the slate as if they had never been. I did not doubt Eddie, or myself. I doubted our ability to be more than grains of sand over which the tide washes.

At first I tried to be busy. Small things had to be done. I had neglected them, had to catch up. Those busy little actions did not last; they fell off me like dead leaves off a tree. The creeping paralysis of depression set in.

I felt that I was caught in a trap. I watched the trap slowly close on me.

Immediately after Eddie went, I wrote to Feli and Jean. I had to be careful how I wrote, for letters were opened and checked. My "very old friend", *Ingenieur* Deichsler from Brno, and I had decided ... The letter, they told me later, threw them into a fair panic. On an impulse I added a PS to it: could Jean please send me a note 'confirming' that he held himself responsible for my financial up-keep, just in case of further enquiries.

I do not know what made me add that paragraph. My guardian angel?

Their answer came by return of post: blessings for my engagement; they hoped I had given my choice much thought. The required note, 'to whom it may concern', was enclosed; so was some money from Feli. Their letter came with the afternoon post. The police came next morning at six, three days after Eddie's departure.

No light-hearted attempts at looking glamorous this time! I followed Ursel's direct and indirect instructions, took my prepared rucksack and the blankets, and led Tova to Madame Davasze.

In the police-station there was a queue of women and old men patiently sitting on benches. This time interviews were held in a separate room; people were called up by name, entered the room, never came out again. It was unnerving.

It took time. Time ticks away. Terror builds up. You wander from terror to frozen calm and back to terror again. Hours pass.

In the interview-room there was one man sitting behind a desk littered with files. He did not look up when I entered. He said:

"Take a seat! Can I see your papers, please. What are your means of livelihood?" without looking up.

I handed him the whole packet of letters and references, and the newly arrived money for good measure. I told him that I was giving English lessons as well.

The officer in charge went speedily through the letters, handed them and the money back to me, said: "*Très bien, merçi, Mademoiselle. Au revoir, Mademoiselle*" and waited for me to go. I had trouble stuffing the letters and money back into my handbag and collecting my gear. My hands were shaking. The man finally looked up.

"If everyone's papers were as much in order as yours are, Mademoiselle, our work would be much reduced," he said sharply. I suppose he meant well. I wanted to tell him that not everyone could be lucky.

One left by a different door from the one through which one came in, that was all. The idea that people who entered that room were never seen again was ill-founded.

To contact Ernest was the next item on my list. He was not to be found. I never saw him again.

I tried the Czech Club, the Legation, music-publishers. I remembered how very pale and drawn he had looked that afternoon, when he brought Eddie. I had hoped it was the light on the landing. I had wanted to run after him, when he left so quickly. I had felt something was not right.

I had not realized that he was saying 'Goodbye' to me in his own way.

Ernest died in a diabetic coma, so I was told much later by the Czech Red Cross. They called it 'an accident'.

Accident? Victim of circumstances? Suicide, while the
balance of his mind was disturbed? One can take one's pick
among the platitudes.

I could not see that he had much to look forward to. With
the requirements of his diabetes he was familiar, having coped
successfully for years.

We were close. Perhaps, in some future life, I can make up
to him what I owe him in this one.

During the autumn weeks the atmosphere in Paris
deteriorated fast. Gone was that little bit of courage and
determination which the first shock had engendered. The men
had gone or were going. The justification for their absence was
not clear. There was no war! There were no battles! They sat
in the cold and the mud for no reason. The lack of events, of
news, led to unrest; the unrest started suspicions. In the
empty streets of Paris rumours ran riot. The foreigners! The
fifth column! It was all the fault of the foreigners. What? All!

It is so simple!

Coffee-houses continued to be raided, the Café du Dôme
two or three times a day. Police were stationed at every corner
of the Boulevard Montparnasse; as soon as you showed
yourself, you were asked for your papers. Madame Devasze
had the Sécurité Nationale as a daily visitor now.

I had glimpses of Sven from a distance; he had transferred
from the Dôme to the Coupole. I did not dare go near him for
he was nearly always drunk and abusive. Peter continued to
write from Switzerland. Was I sure that he could not return to
France, could not volunteer to fight? I was sure! His letters
were an embarrassment; I had to answer them knowing that
mail was opened.

André had at last received the visas he required and was
ready to leave. (He came to say goodbye and bought one of
Jean's paintings, a small Brittany landscape. Jean wrote that I
should keep the money.) Otherwise there was only Boulonski,
the Pole, now 'Monsieur Boulon'.

While I waited for letters from Eddie, which first did not
come at all, later arrived infrequently and said little; while I
wrote letters to Eddie, which tried to sound cheerful, sounded

hollow to me and did not seem to arrive; while French soldiers sat bored in trenches along the northern borders of France and along the Maginot Line; while they came home on leave, drank too much red wine, infected their wives, mothers, sisters and children with their discontent and suspicions, and were an unpleasant sight in their drunkenness; while spy-mania ran amok – I diligently attended to the progress in English of this stiff, emasculated and miserable elderly man.

Misery was followed by horror.

A letter from Feli and Jean said that Jean's regiment was being moved. He had to go to Fontainebleau before going further north – could I come and meet them at Fontainebleau?

I went to the police station with the letter and obtained a one-day permit for Fontainebleau.

It was a dismal meeting. We were polite to each other like strangers. I explained about Eddie. In the end we found ourselves with nothing to say.

I was desolate when I came away. It was dark by the time I left them. I sat next to the window in the train, looking into a black-out curtain. Suddenly there was a commotion in the compartment, shouts, screams. Upright French citizens were beating a man up and had pushed him down on the floor. People from other compartments came and peered in by the door.

The man screamed that he had not done anything, and they all screamed back that yes, he had, he was a spy, he had listened to their conversation, he had asked where they were going. They dragged the poor chap out into the corridor; it seemed that the whole coach was now joyfully joining in, beating and kicking. The man was pouring blood.

I did nothing to help him. I had a foreign accent. My turn next? They would have beaten me up as well.

The man was in poor shape by the time we reached Paris. They dragged him off to the police-station. I do not know what he was supposed to have spied on. I could not see that there were military secrets abounding in the compartment. There was no military personnel at all in that coach.

I left the train and was sick at the edge of the platform. I still felt sick when I reached home.

There was a letter from Eddie. It sounded sad. His men had

started Christmas preparations, but he was not likely to get leave.

Christmas! I had forgotten about Christmas. It would be Eddie's first Christmas without his family. Where might they be? In a concentration camp? His mother was seventy, his daughter seven.

And what was I going to do for Christmas? Buy Tova some special offal and my only other companion, the electric fire, a Christmas tree?

Why did I not go to Agde? We had said for better or for worse. I spent the night walking up and down in the flat. Why did I not go to Agde for Christmas? At first it seemed a daring idea; after five minutes I could not understand why I had not thought of it before. It was the most natural thing in the world.

High-heeled shoes, best clothes. I went to the police-station with my little bundle of letters. I even took Tova. My conviction carried me on a cloud into the lion's den.

They said it would take a fortnight for the permit to come through. *If* it was granted! That made 22nd December the fateful day.

I wrote to Eddie. I wrote to Jean and Feli. I told Monsieur Boulon. I listened to him demurely. I let him finish his spiel. Then I laughed in his face.

Money for fares was a problem. I had some francs left from selling Jean's painting, but not enough. I borrowed some from Madame Davasze. I went back to spaghetti and coffee.

Eddie wrote every day now, twice a day at times.

I was one spaghetti-filled mass of concentrated waiting. I waited through the days, through the nights, awake and in my sleep. I did not allow myself to dwell on the possibility that the permit might be refused.

On the 22nd I was at the police commissariat at nine a.m. The policeman pretended to be very huffy. Why had I not come before? The permit had been there for two whole days! Then they smiled at me, told me not to forget to send them a card from Agde! "*Joyeux Noel!*" I thought: "Dear God, they are human!"

I took Tova and my suitcase and went to the station – praying for my guardian angel to go with me.

10

At the station everyone runs for a place as soon as they are allowed to board the train. Unnecessarily they scramble for seats in compartments which remain half-empty. We leave at 3 p.m.

At eleven in the morning we run into Sète. Here I have to change. There is a chance that Eddie might be there, might fetch me, if he can get away.

He is not there. The little train which is to take me to Agde is late. It comes from the Côte Basque and stops at every station on the way.

When it comes, it is crowded with people from the south, all chattering excitedly at the top of their voices in a slang I hardly understand. They eat huge sandwiches, and Tova refuses to lie under the seat any longer. She sits up in front of the munching people, staring at them, drooling; she is embarrassing; she is in the way.

At every station I ask if this is Agde. A soldier takes pity on me. It is half an hour to Agde, he explains. I will recognize it: first comes a hill, the Mont St Loup, then the train will go round the hill.

No, I am not calmed. With my case and Tova, I edge out of the compartment, stand in the gangway, an obstacle to others. The soldier still tries to reassure me. He will tell me when we come to Agde and will hand my luggage out.

I try to contain myself. I can hear the people in the compartment telling each other in excited voices about the strange foreign soldiers in Agde. They have uprooted trees from the forest and replanted them in the square.

It does seem odd. Then I realize that they are fir-trees, put up in the square as Christmas trees. Relief sweeps over me.

Christmas trees! Christmas is being prepared!

We are at Agde. The soldier, true to his promise, tells me to get out, opens the doors, hands me my case, says: "*Bonne chance!*" It seems frighteningly sudden, that arrival. The train goes off again.

I look around. I can see Eddie far away. I cannot understand why he is so far away. I have not noticed that I am standing at the far end of the platform. Tova begins pulling on her lead, for she has recognized Eddie, and she has no inhibitions. I shout at the dog to sit down, and I stand still, paralysed. My voice sounds shockingly high and sharp to me.

Eddie comes up to us. He wears a trench-coat and an officer's cap, with one blond curl escaping from under it. Surprisingly he holds a small riding-crop in his hand.

I take in every move, every line, as he walks towards us. The familiar walk, slightly bent forward, head on one side, one shoulder pulled higher than the other, the lop-sided smile. He seems small, smaller than I remember. No, it only seems so because there is an exceptionally tall soldier, young and bearded, walking close behind him. The beard looks odd on the soldier's baby-face.

Eddie stands beside me. He looks at me, and I look at him, and the weeks we have spent apart stand solidly between us. Then Eddie says something in Czech to the young soldier, and my case is being whisked away.

"You brought Tova?" Eddie sounds astonished. Not to bring Tova had never occurred to me! "Yes, of course!" I am immediately on the defensive. We are walking side by side out of the station.

"I heard yesterday that I shall be getting leave in January," says Eddie. "On the first."

"Leave! Why didn't you tell me? I could have waited for you in Paris."

"I'm glad that you are here." But Eddie's words do not reach me.

We come to a little bridge. Eddie explains that the river below is the Hérault, that Agde was once a port, not long ago, fifty years perhaps, but the port has silted up. Now Sète is the port, and Agde has become a market town; the sea is five kilometres away, at Grau. I hardly listen. This has nothing to do with me. I wonder what I am doing here, in Agde, walking beside an unknown man along an unknown street.

"This is *the* hotel of Agde," Eddie says, pointing with his riding-crop to a shabby building. (Why does he have a riding-crop? There are no horses!) We have come to the square with the Christmas trees, but even the sight of the Christmas trees evokes no response.

"Would you like a coffee?" Eddie asks. There are several coffee-houses around the square.

"No, thank you."

We turn, walk on, come to a cathedral. "Twelfth-century," explains Eddie. "Two minutes from home now." He informs me that one of his friends has lent him his flat for a week. "The best flat in Agde," he says proudly.

The street becomes very narrow, very dirty. To me, it seems that all the people who are not watching from the windows, are watching from the street, surrounded by happily playing, exceedingly dirty children. Observed by watchful eyes, we enter one of the houses, climb a dank stone staircase. Eddie has a key, opens the door, and we are standing in a small entrance-hall. Hooks on the wall to hang your coat up, no furniture, no space for furniture, two rooms going off the hall. Eddie opens a cupboard, which contains a sink with a cold-water tap. "Isn't the flat nice?" he says. There is a window, thank God, there is a window! From the window one can see the river, angry, yellow water flowing rapidly towards the sea.

"It's lovely."

The young soldier re-appears. His name is Markovitch. He has brought the case; now he is told to light a fire in the stove and to heat some water, so that I can have hot water to wash with. Markovitch laboriously begins to feed the stove with little bits of wood – no, they will not catch alight. They are damp, he explains in Czech. It seems to me that several years pass while we wait silently for the wood to catch fire, and that to look at the angry yellow river during that time is my only salvation.

At last Markovitch, the Yugoslav with the bearded baby-face, succeeds; the stove is alight. Water is getting hot – would I like coffee, Eddie again wants to know. My steady refusal of this well-established stand-by puzzles him. I would have loved a coffee, but I cannot bear the thought of another obstacle, another delay. Delay of what? I do not know.

"All right," Eddie says. "Have a wash now. I'll wait for you in the other room. We'll light the open fire in there later." Markovitch leaves. I obediently begin to wash and put on clean clothes.

Eddie is smoking when I join him in the other room. He offers me a chair, a cigarette. Then he begins to talk.

He talks a lot. The words flow past me as the river flows past outside. I hear them, but it seems to me that they are spoken behind a closed door. He says that he has thought things over and over during our separation. He does not want to tie me down. If I have decided that I do not want to marry him, he quite understands, he will give me back my liberty. If I do not want to continue living with him after the war, he will understand, he will give me back my liberty. He seems terribly intent on giving me back my liberty! I am puzzled! I cannot understand what he means, what he is talking about. I think he is telling me, as politely as he can, that he has changed his mind.

Then he gets up, starts pacing up and down – quite difficult in that small room – and says in his most serious, pompous way:

"If we are still alive after the war and still together ..." He stops, smiles his lop-sided smile at me, "and if we don't want to go back to Czechoslovakia, or can't go back, then we will try to go to Canada, all right? To the woods, we spoke about ... you remember? Build a house, or a log cabin, with a brook at the bottom of the garden and a hot spring. I'll have a job at one of the sawmills, you'll be at home. You'll have children. You want children, don't you?"

The dream is back, the picture-postcard dream! And Thomas! Of course, Thomas! The boy with the dancing dark eyes, with the bright confident smile – how could I have forgotten him so completely for so long.

It is all in the eye of the beholder!

When Eddie had finished his long speech, I was no longer in an ice-cold, mean little flat at the end of a dark, dirty stone staircase, looking on to a yellow, raging river.

Nor was I any longer alone in the dark.

Nor was there a trap closing on me.

We were two. We had come together. Together we had a dream about a future, for which together we would fight as best we could.

You can find heaven anywhere. The great thing is to remember that you did find it, even if only for a fleeting moment. Whatever comes afterwards, that moment is yours.

The 23rd December 1939 – that was the day I got married, and the flat in Agde the place I got married in. What was left to resolve was indeed important – official blessings and the right documents, but it had nothing to do with 'us'.

Next evening we celebrated Christmas three times: first, around the Christmas trees with the whole regiment and most of the locals, Eddie with his company, I on the fringe. The soldiers sang the carols of their country; homesickness, grief and hope echoed around foreign firs in a foreign square.

Then at an official mess-dinner, a stiff social event. I felt uncomfortable, tried my best smile and could feel the cracks beneath it.

Then 'at home', at the flat, with two of Eddie's friends, a writer and a lawyer, both privates in the Czech army. We lit the open fire, and though it poured smoke into the room, still, it gave the illusion of warmth. We lit the candles on our small Christmas tree, and opened some bottles of cheap champagne.

As a Christmas it had little chance. Eddie and I were glad to be together. The missing 'good will to all men' choked us. The tears we did not cry were not just our own, they were everyone's tears.

I remember little of the few days in Agde. The last months had been frightening. I felt shy. I had a cold. I hid behind it.

I waited in the flat for Eddie. Friends of his would drop in in the evening, the writer, nicknamed '*mon poète*', usually among them. Eddie would eagerly come home, immediately shoot out again to return with wine, fruit, cake, some other special thing, and go despairingly through his pockets next morning, wondering what had become of his money. It was a regular occurrence. It was a very 'Eddie' occurrence. Shades of Dostoevsky.

Eddie's CO strongly advised us to go and see the consul in

Paris during the three-day leave and gave us a letter to him. Our HQ in Béziers was a shambles, he said. We had an extraordinarily peaceful journey to Paris. Nobody asked for our tickets or my travel-permit. In Paris I reported back to the police.

The three days we spent at the Legation, making the necessary arrangements, returning with the witnesses, returning for additional signatures. The duplicate documents would be ready in a week, we were told. Could I come back for them then?

This time I saw Eddie to his train. We would see each other again in four weeks time, when he would have another three days' leave – compassionate leave to get married.

I crawled back to Feli's flat in despair, convinced that the parting, waiting, meeting, parting, would never end.

Feli and Jean came home on a fortnight's leave soon after Eddie had gone. The flat became warm and alive.

I was fully engaged in the final battle of the Paper War during their stay, had twice been back to the Legation for the duplicate certificates, cried bitter tears at the Consul and obtained them on my third visit.

It was only the beginning of a weird and unattractive dance, one step forward and three steps back. The Procureur de la République required written approval for the marriage from the Czech military authorities before giving the certificates his official approval. The Préfecture de la Police demanded certificates of domicile proving that I had been in Paris for over a year. I brought the certificates from Madame Mollet and Madame Davasze – not good enough! Permission to remain in France for another year was required from the Ministry of the Interior.

To see the right official took a morning's or a full day's waiting, the correct consent, approval, permission by one of his superiors two days to a week, all the documents signed and stamped by the Ministry of Foreign Affairs. The stamps cost a fortune. Time was running short. I had three days in hand to get Eddie's certificate of domicile. No trouble there, he only had to prove a six months' stay in Paris and had arrived nearly a year ago.

I met my Waterloo in a dingy side-street of Paris. Yes, yes,

Mr Deichsler had been staying at the hotel nearly ten months, but not officially! It would be more than their licence was worth to sign a six months' certificate! Four months. No more! Four months was not enough. They dated the certificate 31st May.

It was an unexpected blow. I came home in tears. Feli said nothing and gave me a cup of coffee. The light of battle was in her eyes.

Without exchange of words, we went over to Jean's drawing-equipment in the studio, erased part of the five (May) and with infinite care substituted a three (March).

The people in the hotel had done me a favour after all. It would have been much more difficult to turn a six into a three.

Feli came with me next day when I went to the Mairie to hand the papers in. It was just as well, my heart beat so loudly I felt sure the lady who took the papers would hear it. What prison sentence was I likely to get?

Three days later we finally made it, on the last day of Eddie's leave.

Gold chairs with red velvet seats, luscious red velvet curtains in an otherwise bare room, greeted us at the Mairie. There were several couples sitting pale and nervous at the very edge of the chairs, one couple per row. We were the last one.

The man who was to marry us had a wide blue ribbon across his chest. He looked bored and impatient, and spoke fast and with utter indifference; he had nothing to do with any of us. Eddie shouted his 'yes', and I whispered mine. When it came to signing the marriage-certificate, my hand shook so much that I could hardly write. All of a sudden we were standing outside the Mairie on the Place St Sulpice in Paris, and we were married.

We ended up in the Coupole. The manager rose to the occasion: 'best wishes' and a bottle of champagne for 'one of his most loyal clients'. We ate a lot, drank a lot, talked a lot, and I felt confused from start to finish.

Eddie left the same day; I had to wait for a travel-permit. Till my new papers came through, I still had to obey established police procedure.

Three days after my wedding, I was at the railway station again, this time with two large trunks and Tova. A married woman, a friendly alien, joining her husband, a serving officer, and his regiment in the South of France. Very honourable indeed!

Rules had been satisfied! The law had been satisfied. All was well.

Not quite all. It takes years to overcome so much resentment.

PART TWO

Grains of Sand

.

1

On impulse I took my Austrian lodencape with me on this second journey to Agde, a garment of tent-like proportion, designed to keep you and your rucksack protected from wind and rain in mountains, as unsuitable for the South of France as for townwear. Perhaps I thought it a link between my former existence and my future.

During the long, dreary night journey south I sat, my head hidden in the woollen folds, trying to sleep, while small anxieties rushed through my brain like restless ants. What was it going to be like to be married? Did I, in fact, have any talent for married life, for the life of an officer's wife in a garrison town? Where were we going to live? Eddie had said nothing about our future home.

My fears grew with the darkness, receded with dawn. Eddie was not at the station in Sète – I had not expected him to be there, though I had hoped perhaps. He was not at the station in Agde either.

I looked wildly around. Then I sat down on one of the trunks. Tova sat down beside me. Within seconds I had changed from bright-eyed bride to unseeing refugee, eternally sitting on her case. When Tova started to whimper, I was sightless.

As Tova pulled frantically at her lead, I dragged my eyes back from nowhere and tiredly observed a figure far away, rushing towards us. It could not be Eddie, there was no tall soldier with him. But it was Eddie, flushed from running, left shoulder pulled higher than the right one, the lop-sided smile more lop-sided than ever.

"I am so sorry ... the company ..."

It was a bright sunny day in Agde. You could smell the start

of spring. The man with Eddie was small and resentful, the
sight of my two cases doing nothing to cheer him up. Eddie
and I were walking arm in arm out of the station.

That was my first inkling that I had married not just Eddie
but his company, and his batman as well. I did not mind
about the company; I was less keen on the batman.

Eddie did not have the afternoon off – the company! – but
there was time for a coffee and a bite to eat. There was
tomorrow and the day after and the day after that. The
anticipation of time was intoxicating. He would be back early
in the evening, Eddie said. Unfortunately there was a dinner-
dance in the officers' mess that night. Of course we had to
attend! A monthly event. Important for morale! "You do have
an evening dress, don't you?" – I did have an evening dress. I
had brought it with me. And my travelling-iron. I was pleased
with myself: the first challenge of my new existence had been
met head on.

Eddie took me 'home' before he disappeared again, and
home turned out to be the single room that he had occupied
since he first arrived, on the first floor of a modern cottage.
One other room was occupied by two French officers; there
was a washroom, a separate toilet. The washroom had a sink
and running cold water; the toilet was the modern variety.
Newly arrived, I had no idea of their stunning importance.
The cottage had a pretty garden, in which a tall white-haired
woman, dressed in black, was hoeing.

I sat in the room and waited for the arrival of my trunks,
which came so late that Eddie came only seconds after them.
Now there was hardly time to find the evening dress, the shoes
that went with it, the right handbag, the iron. Eddie discreetly
retired to the washroom, returned washed, changed, freshly
shaved. I was ready! I fervently hoped that I looked better
than I felt.

The party disclosed a problem which I stupidly had not
anticipated: the language problem. Obviously the official
language was Czech, and German, known to nearly everyone,
was taboo. I was not the only one there who did not speak
Czech, but I was ignorant of the existence of fellow-sufferers. I
was also unsure about Army etiquette. Desperately I tried to

appear pleasing in French – there was some justification for speaking French.

It was well after midnight when we reached home. At quarter to six next morning Ludovic, the new batman, marched into our room. "Beg to report, Sir, a quarter to six, Sir." I dived under the blankets. I had not been warned. I felt intensely embarrassed that an unfamiliar soldier should find me in bed with a man.

Eddie had just time to pass me a cup of the coffee which Ludovic had brought in, when the batman re-appeared. I could not dive under the covers, I now had a cup of coffee in my hands. "What will the lieutenant wear today – long trousers or breeches? High boots or shoes? A black or a khaki tie? What shirt?" It seemed a dazzling choice. Ludovic collected the chosen garments and marched out.

What had happened to Markovitch? What had become of the flat? Markovitch had been neither so noisy nor so military; in fact I had never noticed his early-morning appearance at Christmas. The flat, of course, had had two rooms!

Markovitch had not enjoyed his role as batman, Eddie explained. Markovitch, with the bearded baby-face, born in Yugoslavia of Czech parents, working in Egypt as hotel-porter at the outbreak of the war, had joined to fight for his country, not to fulfil a domestic role. He had shaved off his beard and joined the Infantry, drill, marches, fatigues included. Markovitch was happy now.

The flat was occupied by its rightful owner, who had been absent on leave at Christmas time. There were no other flats available in Agde. We were lucky to have a room in a house with modern facilities. In any case, the regiment would soon move.

Ludovic was a splendid batman, Eddie added proudly, a pearl among his kind!

To me Ludovic seemed a pain in the neck! He obviously resented my arrival – why had his lieutenant found it necessary to complicate things by getting married? He was a nasty little weasel of a man with darting brown eyes, small, wiry, devious. I had ignored him at the station, I was pre-occupied then. I had ignored his display of martyrdom when he finally condescended to bring the cases up to the room. But I was the new girl in a school in which he was well established. Would I kindly vacate room and washroom by nine so he could clean them? There were other things he had to do; he could not hang about.

At the foot of the stairs I met my landlady, *la Veuve* Audouy, together with her daughter and granddaughter. They were ready to go out, to the market. *"Bonjour, Madame. Ça va, Madame?"* Had I slept well? Was I going shopping? Was there anything I might need?

She is the widow of a colonial officer, Madame Audouy tells me proudly, and I am promptly introduced to the photo of Monsieur Audouy, who stares at me with beetling brows out of a heavy silver frame. The daughter, Rose, looks like her father. Dark-haired, dark-eyed, she studies me with open curiosity. Her daughter, a fair and fragile child of five, has the blue eyes of the grandmother. *"Bonjour, Madame"*, says the child in a surprisingly broad accent from between the folds of her grandmother's skirt.

La Veuve Audouy is tall, straight and slim, aged about fifty. She has white hair and the movements of a girl, every move a rippling fold in that long wide skirt. A widow, she wears only black. When she goes out, she takes her apron off and puts a black shawl around her shoulders. She does not just speak, she mimes what she says. The first floor – a sweeping gesture – will be Rose's flat after the war, when her husband, a colonial officer as well,' returns from Béziers. In the meantime – a shrug of the shoulders – one has to eat. Her hands put food into her mouth. Money is short, runs like sand through your fingers – and now there is sand running through her fingers. One has to live. Will I let her know if I need anything? *"Alors, bonne journée, Madame."*

What a lovely woman!

Ludovic had left. I could go upstairs and unpack. At midday I met Eddie in one of the small cafés on the square. Tongue-tied we sat in the pale sunshine, new to each other in our new role as man and wife. He would be home at six, Eddie said.

He was. Behind him, arriving in dribs and drabs, came a stream of soldiers. They had come to wash, shave, have a cup of coffee and chat, indulge in the luxury of a real WC. Camp lacked amenities, I was told. Every officer who could offer mains water and a decent toilet, had his trail of other ranks, till ten, when the camp gates closed.

Eddie's sergeant, Welzek, was among the visitors, keeping some sort of order, looking as if carved in wood. And there was a formerly rich and spoiled youngster, Toni, whom I had known in Vienna, a private now who does not speak Czech and whom everyone calls 'Schweik'.

Those first thirty-six hours as a married woman were annihilating; the next few days not much better. I mainly remember feeling tired and confused. I do not even know if I felt happy or unhappy at the time. Probably neither.

I did not get a chance to settle down, even to come to grips with cooking a midday meal on a one-flame alcohol-burner. Inexplicably I was struck down with a heavy attack of sciatica, unable to straighten up, stand, sit or lie in comfort, my eyes now firmly on the ground, were it cobbles, lino, wooden floors or earth.

Advice rained down on me, every soldier proffering his own special medication, from '*mon poète*'s' vitamin pills to Welzek's mustard plaster. Some evil jokers in the company whispered to Toni that there was a sure-fire cure; it just needed a bit of guts – of course, if he was squeamish ...?

Toni, the softy, the boy who had not grown up, with the devoted eyes, living in an aura of total confusion, arrived with the still bloody skin of a freshly shot and skinned cat.

I veered towards hysteria. Eddie dashed out, buried the skin in the *Veuve* Audouy's manure-heap and came back later with the doctor of the Second Regiment, a man with a prematurely lined face, who said little.

He had no need to speak, his eyes spoke for him, eyes which had seen it all. He had sailed out with a contingent of Jewish emigrants to Palestine, had been five months at sea before being turned back to port. Later he made it to the Holy Land; now he was back.

A series of injections enabled me to straighten up again. Toni, who did not know about the doctor, lived with the illusion that his sacrifice had not been in vain. Eddie said he had his work cut out to keep Toni from worse things than being teased. I felt convinced that the numerous cats of Agde all knew and looked at me with malevolent eyes.

While my eyes had been forced to the ground, spring had come to the South of France and was beguiling. The Czech Legion was five months old; a First and Second Regiment had been formed; a Third was in the course of formation. Agde was overcrowded, and rumour had it that part of the First Regiment would soon be moved out.

2

The ancient fortress city of Agde, dating from the sixth century BC, is quite small. Two rows of houses built closely opposite each other wind themselves up and around the Mont St Loup. No sanitation but a donkey-cart with a tank on it, and slop-buckets with a 25-centime piece on their lids in front of the houses. I had thought that donkey-cart very romantic at Christmas, when I had not realized its function. The houses were white-washed, built on black lava rock. The people of the South call Agde '*La Ville Noire du Sud*'!

The inhabitants were not so concerned with the city's ancient history as with its more recent one. Pirates from Morocco, they said, had invaded the port a couple of hundred years ago. The inhabitants – not they themselves, the other inhabitants – were descendants of these pirates. The latter had not multiplied fast: two hundred years after their arrival, there were still only six thousand people living in Agde. Had the pirates found what they had been looking for? Were their descendants hiding in caves under the black lava rock? Whoever I talked to denied being 'Aghatois'. Their parents had moved in when it was a fishing-port; they themselves had come when it became a market town; there were no grandparents.

Spread at the foot of the Mont St Loup, the new Agde had begun. A market place, the square with its hotel, cinema and small cafés, simple modern cottages like that of the *Veuve* Audouy. On the outskirts were the well-built, solid barracks of the Colonial Service, not far from them the Czech army camp. It was surrounded by rusty barbed wire, having housed 'Red Spaniards' during the Spanish Civil War, Italians before that, and was bad, I gathered. Four months of rain had turned the ground around it into a quagmire. To begin with, the people of Agde had been hostile to the troops, but they were friendly now: their goods were marked up in Czech; the children shouted the Czech greeting '*Nasdar*' in the streets.

This was the third spring since Hitler had marched into Austria, and I fell for it. I fell in love with the *Veuve* Audouy, whom I met four or five times a day and never in vain. Had I slept well? Was I going to the market? What was I going to look for? All information she received at the market was promptly passed on to me: the butcher was going to get fresh liver later on; there was some excellent fish today at the fishmonger's stall. – "*Ça va? Tous va bien?*" – And after lunch: "*C'était bon? Ç'a réussi?*" In the afternoon it was a chat over the garden rake, hoe or fork. Soon I found her waiting with me for news from Feli and Jean and did not even remember having spoken to her about them.

This was spring and playtime, the ghastly autumn and winter months, the last two years, pushed into the background, though not forgotten. I fell in love with the market and the singing southern voices; the whole scene was like an opera – one waited for the music to strum up.

Market shopping came first, but there were other shops, the grocer, the butcher, the baker. Sometimes I met army personnel in the shops and noticed that they would surreptitiously be handed bits of wood, or tin, oddments. Surprising. The bits of material would disappear under coats and jackets. Eddie too had a mania for collecting odd pieces, which he stacked up in our room, marching to camp with his collection hidden under his coat. I asked him once what they were for, but his answer cannot have made an impression, for I do not remember it. Playtime!

The grocer's was called the 'Dock St Clare'. Shopping there was an experience. The Dock St Clare was run by two elderly women, called 'the girls' – '*les filles*' – by the population. They were big and stout and loved each other dearly, and whenever you entered the shop, you landed in the middle of their eternal argument as to who should serve and who should rest. Shopping at the Dock St Clare was down on my time-table for half an hour, but it needed perseverance. It was also unavoidable, for theirs was the only real grocery store.

'*La Boucherie*' was run by a lady who opened and closed the shop according to how her ailing mother felt. The baker I left to the last. I went there at noon, when the bread was just ready to come out of the ovens.

At noon the different companies would be marching home from morning exercises. The lady at the bakery would get excited about them, stop serving, come to the door and, while watching them from the doorway, ask all sorts of questions.

I got my bread when the companies had passed.

One lunch-time I made some remark to Eddie about the smart marching, happily singing troops, and he quietly said,

"They are not singing because they are happy. They are told to do so."

"All soldiers?"

"Ours especially."

The way he said it made me drop out of the cuckoo clouds. He sounded resigned – full of fatherly patience.

Ordered to sing? Ours especially? I had been proud of our troops, for they livened up the sight of this little historic fortress city under the first rays of a pale sun. The sight of the lads coming out of the barracks in the lengthening evenings and strolling aimlessly about had struck me as romantic! Playtime? I had been living in a fool's paradise, where everything seemed colourful and gay, touched by the magic of spring.

The spring stayed. The rest went. I was ashamed of myself.

I asked Eddie to tell me about the Czech army, the men, the difficulties – the truth, our truth – to lift the conspiracy of silence – I realized that there had been one.

"All right," he said, "if you want me to, I will." We would close our door for the evening, so that we could talk in peace, he would tell 'the boys'.

Playtime, the fool's paradise, had not lasted long. It had been nice while it lasted.

I am no longer ashamed of it. One has to survive life somehow.

3

During the afternoon that followed that lunchtime, I battled with bitterness, with self-pity. The new impending doom brought it all out.

We had ignored politics in Vienna, my friends and I, thought them contemptible. We went to this café to watch the chess-players, to that one to look in on bridge, to the Café Mozart to listen to discussions about music, but never to any café where politics were discussed. Politics were boring, something to laugh about in the sports-train travelling to and from the mountains. The murder of Dollfuss, the uprising in the suburban streets of Vienna, had made a dent in our gilded armour, but only a small one.

Hitler's rise to power in Germany? Germany was different!

The crooked cross painted on the outside of mountain huts or on rocks at the edge of the Danube? Fun to pick up that challenge, paint them over, engage in scuffles.

The warnings of a colleague at the paper:

"They are coming. Why don't you believe me? I do know. It is all organized. They are coming ..." The man was insane!

Since then I had lived the consequences of politics, and now their dark wings were going to overshadow the temporary light relief of the recent weeks.

The first problem, so Eddie told me that evening, arose from being on 'foreign soil'. The surroundings in which the Czechs were living and training were unfamiliar, frequently hostile, the different language an additional barrier. The Legion was accepted on sufferance, officers and men made to feel that this was so. There was no contact with home, but terrifying rumours of reprisals, deportations to concentration camps, exterminations. German broadcasts added to the anxiety: they had started in early October, mentioning the 'pirates' or the 'beggars' of Agde and were singularly well informed.

Active resistance to the Legion by the 'overlords', the French officers in charge, caused further soul-destroying and unexpected hardships.

France was split. The Czech garrison in the south fell between extremes of the two factions: elderly right-wing brass-hats, called out of retirement, and young Leftists, sent to Agde as a punishment. The right-wing faction was superior in number and seniority.

The French C-in-C of the Czech Legion, sent to early retirement because he had at some time blotted his copy-book and now called back, was a member of the 'Action Française', and had been – possibly still was – a member of the 'Cagoulards'. One of his adjutants belonged to the 'Autonomists of Brittany', another violently right-wing group. He was well known in Agde, having been in charge of the 'Red Spaniards' when they occupied the camp, and had himself fought for Franco before being sent there. He was an admirer of Hitler and of Nazi doctrine and methods. Although his enthusiasm for these was officially curbed, his opportunities of making life hell for the Legion were considerable. His counterpart, the other adjutant, was a young Democrat, much persecuted by his colleagues. He was later to join a Czech unit.

Opportunities for passive resistance and sabotage abounded. The camp was foul, standing in a sea of mud, the barracks so dilapidated that it was impossible to keep out weather or dirt; there were holes in the roofs, windows without glass, broken doors, broken wooden bunks, appalling and insufficient sanitation. There was, for instance, no ditch for kitchen refuse. Repairs by the Czechs were forbidden, as was digging additional trenches. Material lying freely about and suitable for repairs was declared 'out of bounds' – hence the secret collections under jackets and coats. Improvements to the camp could be carried out only under French supervision, which had to be applied for in writing, but since letters containing such applications did not arrive at their destination, French supervision could not arrive. Repairs carried out in secret by officers or men had to be torn down if discovered. "Against orders!"

If, after months of delay, improvements were carried out – the kitchen refuse-trench was finally approved, and orders for it issued – events had overtaken the original application, and the influx of men into the camp made the operation inadequate, if not futile. There were numerous 'kitchen trench' incidents.

Training of troops offered another opportunity to foul them up. French instructors had been promised for October, for there were differences between Czech and French battle-training, and the founder-officers of the Legion were to a large extent officers of the Reserve. Though French instructors did not arrive, the men could not be left idle, and so physical training and parades took over for a while. The instructors did eventually come:

"They arrived precisely one month after we had given up waiting and started training our troops our way! Now all the troops have to start from scratch again.

"Worst of all," Eddie continued, "there now is strife within the Legion, between those officers who left Czechoslovakia just before or after Munich and those who have come out recently, five months after the declaration of war via the underground pipeline. And the German broadcasts keep the pot boiling."

Comradeship and enthusiasm in the original group had been tremendous, and idealism had run high. Men had come from all over the world to join. The Czech Commander-in-Chief had flown back from the French Foreign Legion in Syria (contracts between Czechs and the Foreign Legion had contained a release clause in case of war). Together they had faced the deplorable conditions, made worse by the weather of that winter, and had gone without pay for months. Now they were accused of being 'adventurers', of 'having deserted their country in its hour of need', by the young Regulars smuggled out since the beginning of 1940, a different type of officer altogether. Requirements for officer selection had changed, training methods had changed, and, in view of the impending war, length of training had been curtailed. In turn, the new arrivals were suspected of having come only because they were no longer paid in Czechoslovakia, and of being infiltrated as spies.

"Spy activity has undoubtedly increased," Eddie said. "I learn more about Czech troop movement from the German radio than from our headquarters. You know yourself that they mention new arrivals by name. Now they have started to threaten our hosts."

I knew. Daily they promised to hang any of us from the nearest tree or lamp-post when they came – and they were coming, they said. We would not be regarded as prisoners of war: we were traitors. Those French who gave us shelter would be shot. The French population was not impressed by the threats: "*sales boches*" and a shrug of the shoulders.

"The Sûreté Nationale undoubtedly also have their informants among us," Eddie added thoughtfully, and I thought of Ludovic, who had been living in France for over twenty years. I did not say anything. I was glad when Eddie at long last had stopped speaking.

I had asked to know the truth, our truth. Now I knew it.

It changed me. It lifted me out of the confines of my own life, set me down on a wider plane. I did not regret having asked for the truth, although the burden was heavy. To feel as humble as I did feel then is a relief: it frees you of yourself. I did regret that our truth was so bitter.

And who, I wondered late that night, was going to remember us, grains of sand, caught in the storm of our time, struggling against so violent a tide? Struggling and being swept under. Struggling and being tossed onto dry land. Little people, who lived and suffered, survived or died.

Would my story be theirs?

Would there be time to write it?

Would anyone want to know?

4

Two months after my arrival in Agde, it was finally decided that the First Regiment would have to be moved. The place most frequently mentioned was Pézénas, some twenty kilometres away. Pézénas was not able to take the whole of the regiment, so it would have to be split. Eddie was not sure where his company, the Eleventh, would be stationed. This was a pity, for Eddie and I would have liked to go flat-hunting in advance. Any village finally decided upon would be the last stop before the regiment moved north, towards the expected front, before separation.

We decided to take a gamble and have a look at Pézénas on our next free Sunday. The gamble came off.

Pézénas was a gift from the gods. The men found excellent quarters, we found a delicious little house. The sun shone. The spring was beautiful.

The Eleventh Company had their new quarters in an empty warehouse, opposite our cottage. No rusty barbed wire, mud or inhuman conditions; instead, neatly arranged straw-sacks, tidily folded blankets, all equipment shining. Sergeant Welzek strutted up and down between the neat rows as if he had invented the universe. Sent on leave for a fortnight, he returned after three days; everybody had been kind to him, but ... he had been homesick for his boys. Leave is difficult in a foreign country.

My departure from the *Veuve* Audouy had been fraught with emotion. The grey-haired widow made surreptitious use of a corner of her apron; I hugged her as if I had known her all my life and had now to part from her forever. Would I let her know if there was any 'news'? Of course I would. After two months of marriage, news had to be imminent!

Our small house looked out on field after field of blossoming fruit trees on one side, towards the dark, rugged Pyrenees, their peaks hidden in clouds, on the other. The town itself was charming: no black lava foundation, no barrenness, and none of that intrigue and suspicion which had so increasingly poisoned the atmosphere in Agde.

The 'traitor of Stuttgart' on the German radio followed our move faithfully, but he threatened in vain, and the population of Pézénas took no notice. Contact between the inhabitants and us was free and easy. The head of the police department made himself available if help was required and took part in meetings and discussions.

Pézénas was the last stage before amalgamation with the French Army and active participation in the war. This was a great relief to officers and men, a boost to morale. Nevertheless, the number of people on leave, a general dying-down of regimental activities, and cheap red wine led to some complications. Eddie did a private collecting round night after night to prevent his men from falling into the hands of the military police.

While stationed in Pézénas, we met Jean and Feli in Montpellier. They also were on leave, having parked the baby with friends and come south. Jean's regiment was going to be moved to the Dutch border – his men too were short of straw-sacks, blankets and ammunition. I did not mention our difficulties. We met – we still existed! We enjoyed a good meal together – we were still human.

"Helen's and Hans' address in America as a last resort?" Feli asked in a whisper when we parted. We agreed on that.

Pézénas, the gift from the gods, euphoria before the end! The end, we imagined, would come with a flourish. We were wrong. Our end came with a whimper.

It came one Sunday evening. We had arrived home on our newly-bought bicycles, happy, flushed from the ride. There was a message for Eddie at home. Would he join his CO at once?

Marching orders for the regiment? We were surprised. No rumours had preceded them. Half the men were still away on leave. Perhaps some personal need of our new CO? Eddie said he would let me know if he was detained for any length of time.

He came back within minutes. His face was ashen, his left shoulder drawn up high, his hands restless.

He had been ordered back to Agde. Report tomorrow, Monday, at eight. The CO had sent the message around in the morning, but we had been out. Eddie, and fifty other reserve officers, had been ordered to attend a military re-training course.

Eddie paused. I could not see that the news was all that bad. The sting was in the tail, the bit that Eddie was so slow, so reluctant, to give voice to. Their positions, he said at long last, were going to be taken over by the newcomers, the recently arrived Regulars.

Perhaps only temporarily, I suggested. He, Eddie himself, had said ... I stopped. The inane gushing did not help! Would he like something to eat? No? Coffee?

It was a busy night. I had to go and inform our landlord. I had to pack. I produced coffee on a conveyor-belt while trying to collect our things together. From time to time Eddie made valiant attempts to be useful and failed.

We did not go to bed, just lay down for a while. At seven-thirty we were in Agde; Eddie marched off to camp; I went to find *La Veuve* Audouy. She could not put us up. The French officers who had shared a room before were now occupying both rooms. Agde was full to bursting point. "*There isn't space left to house a tiny mouse.*" Le Grau d'Agde was my best bet, she suggested. Not a bad place to be in during the hot months – at the seaside, cool in the evenings. She tried to make the place sound attractive, but her voice lacked conviction. Yes, of course I could leave our hand-luggage with her. What about a cup of coffee before I set off?

It was five kilometres to Grau. The road was long, straight, dusty. It was hot for early morning in April. I was trying to march the cobwebs away.

Wrapped in thought, I marched straight into a young couple returning from Grau: Lieutenant Swenska, one of the young Regulars who had come to Agde in March, with his fiancée, who had joined him from Paris – they were in the middle of their Paper War, hoping to marry soon. Was I going to Grau for the day? Looking for accommodation? Accommodation was scarce, for a Czech colony was already well-established in Grau. They had managed to find a flat that morning, and there was another one to be had next door in the house of an elderly lady. If I hurried ...

"With sanitation?"

"Sort of. A hut in the garden. But mains water!"

I thought that I might be able to do better than that but was defeated by the sight of Grau. It was a seaside slum. No trees, no fields, few gardens, lots of sand. The houses looked mean and shabby. The people looked mean and shabby. I wondered what had happened first: did the people make the place or the place the people?

The flat in the house of the elderly lady was the only one still available. It was expensive. Grau was regarded as a holiday resort, and April the start of the season. The flat had two rooms and a kitchenette, the hut in the garden and a large asparagus bed on the way to the hut. The elderly lady was worried about the dog – did he bite? I was worried about her asparagus bed. Little old ladies are eagle-eyed!

I took the flat and sent a message to Eddie, then I cleaned the place out, went shopping, prepared a meal and put flowers on the table.

Eddie looked sick when he arrived – Swenska brought him in an army car. The training-course was run by some new-comers, subalterns in their early twenties. They had started the military re-training by explaining the mysteries of the gun.

Eddie attended the course for three days; on the fourth he reported sick. He ran a high temperature. An infection, a virus, a breakdown? He was very ill. Our doctor friend from the Second Regiment came out daily to see him.

When Eddie reported back for duty, he was told that it was too late for him to rejoin the course. He was made 'Officer in Charge of Transportation and Troop Movements'.

That last shock changed Eddie. It extinguished hope and damaged pride; it opened the floodgates to the grief and anxiety he had so long repressed. Something in Eddie died that Sunday in Pézénas and was never reborn.

It changed my attitude to the Czech Legion. I bore resentment. One is not always logical. I felt that 'they' had murdered my man.

5

Le Grau d'Agde was not a place to give one courage or hope. There seemed little justification for its existence.

The population had too much time for gossip, too many children playing unsupervised in too much dirt. There was only one family to gladden my heart, Italians, living in a little white-washed cottage opposite our flat. They had a tiny garden full of flowers and vegetables, tended by Bianca, the eldest daughter. She had black hair and black eyes, wore a flower in her hair and sang while she worked. Mama was massive, black-eyed and either in the kitchen or hanging over the garden gate; wherever she was, one could hear her. The little cottage spewed forth black-eyed children in a steady stream. One son served with the Navy, but Papa was there, too old or unfit for service.

Papa was a busy man! He left early in the morning, whistling loudly. He returned late in the afternoon shouting for attention from afar. He returned like a king, was greeted like a king and deposited his spoils of the day as if he had brought back the treasures of the Incas. A bundle of driftwood, a couple of fishes. The Italian family were like peacocks among sparrows.

Shopping? One shop and the butcher's van. The arrival of the butcher's van was the signal for the whole female population to assemble.

The grey women of Grau were in full flight when I arrived one day. They had turned on an elderly woman and were teasing her, their eyes shining. I joined the queue, waiting and wondering if these women were human or a species apart, when the elderly woman turned on her tormentors. With tears streaming down her face, she told them in a loud, singing voice how God had said that those who sinned and repented should be forgiven. The pack fell back in surprise. The butcher's assistant stopped serving, just stood, a piece of meat in his hands dramatically dripping blood, his mouth hanging open. Carried away by her unexpected success, the old woman began to recite the whole Bible story. The crowd stood still. There was only a subdued mumble when she finished. Now they were all in a hurry to get home. And everywhere lunch was going to be late.

It was not the only local drama we witnessed. There was Eve and her 'lamb'. (Twice a week Eve came to our flat to try to get the sand out.) One morning she arrived, shouting and crying:

"*Ah, mon Dieu, mon Dieu*, what a catastrophe ... what a disaster! My daughter ... my precious little daughter ... Yvonne, my poor child ... oh my poor innocent little lamb ... she has ruined her life ... she has got herself into trouble ... what am I to do? My husband will kill me ... he will kill the girl if he finds out, the poor innocent child ... she has brought shame on him ... on herself, perhaps it will be best if he kills us all. I wish I'd die, right here ... right now ... on this spot ... *mon Dieu, mon Dieu, quel malheur!*"

Yvonne was sixteen, and the culprit was Bianca's brother.

Eve is ranting herself into a state of high indignation. Wrong has been done to her poor innocent lamb. She will go and see the culprit's mother. She sets off, calling for the Italian mamma from afar.

Their conversation does not take place indoors but over the garden gate! Mamma meets her adversary in Bianca's carefully tended garden, drawing herself up to full height and full width. She listens with attention and dignity to Eve, who begins with great constraint by saying:

"Your son, Madame, has ruined my daughter ..."

The constraint does not last. The laments, the accusations take over, God is once again called upon:

"*Quel malheur, quel désastre, quelle catastrophe!*"

Bianca's mother also calls on God: "*Santo Dio, il Pietro* ... The wicked boy! The sinful child!" She has great trouble hiding the pride she feels. She has obviously decided that she is not going to lag behind in the flow of words. "*Mama mia,* there you work your fingers to the bone, bringing up your children, trying to instil the fear of God into them, trying to teach them to live an honest, decent life ...

"If my boy has sinned," she concludes her insincere tirade, "He will be made to repent! On his next leave Pietro will marry Yvonne. *E basta!*" The culprit's and Yvonne's views on the matter are not required.

The best thing in Grau was the splendid beach. Once Eddie was back at camp, I made full use of it. It became the meeting-place of all the 'foreigners' in Grau and some from Agde.

We were a motley crowd on that beach, relatives of army personnel, camp-followers, the odd soldier or officer who had managed to get away from duties for a while. Eddie and I made friends with two young couples, Margit and her Lieutenant Swenska and seventeen-year-old Hedi and her fiancé, another newly arrived young officer. Margit and Swenska had all their papers together and were on the point of taking them to headquarters in Béziers for officials' stamps and signatures; Hedi, lively, resilient and much in love, was nowhere near so far. She had fled the Sudetenland after the Germans had marched in to 'free' their suppressed brothers and had only recently reached France.

The doctor was left from our friends in Agde; Toni, '*mon poète*', and others had been moved to the front. Agde had become unbearable, we were told: friction, tension, suspicion had reached fever pitch; the waiting game sapped everybody's sanity.

The atmosphere in Grau was not pleasant either, but heavy and threatening, the hot air itself seeming evil, as if the southern sun were hatching dragons' eggs. Life was holding its breath.

Eddie and I lost contact with our dream of a log cabin in Canada. We lost contact with hope. We lost contact with ourselves. We were two grains of sand among others, waiting for the next tidal-wave.

It came. Indeed, it came!

6

Once Hitler's armies had started to move against the West, we found it difficult to keep up with the speed of events. News given out over the radio was restricted. Discussions in Grau and Agde centred around the water defences of Holland and the fortifications of Belgium, but Hitler's troops had passed both and were fighting battles in the north of France!

It did not take long for refugees to arrive – by car, train, lorry, on foot. Bewildered people, with hollow eyes and stricken faces, they dragged pale children after them, carried smaller ones in their arms, loaded with futile bundles of belongings. Some had died on the roads, some given birth on the roads.

The Police Commissioner of Grau became active. Proclamations and orders were read out. Big military kitchens arrived in the villages, set up in market squares. News from the Belgian and Dutch Consulates about relatives began to filter through. The dust of that first earthquake had only just begun to settle when the Belgian King Leopold's surrender was announced.

Transport problems had brought Eddie to Pézénas for the day, and I had gone with him. We were in the lounge of the Grand Hotel when the news of the 'betrayal' came over the radio.

The hotel was inundated with refugees, the lounge crowded. Gasps and exclamations punctuated the announcement. Then came silence.

A dreadful silence. The announcer was droning on, and that big room became still. Slowly minute movements rippled through the mass of people. Heads sank down, shoulders hunched, hands covered faces, tears flowed over others out of wide-open eyes.

After the silence came the storm. Why? The refugees shook with the question 'Why?' which no one could answer. Why did their men have to be killed, their homes bombed, if King Leopold was going to surrender? The question ran through them like a sickness, tore them apart. And while their grief overwhelmed them, the French robed themselves in hostility and suspicion. To these people they had given food and beds. To them they had extended their hand in friendship and compassion. What had happened to their men, the French soldiers, who had been rushed up north to the defence of Holland and Belgium? Where were they?

We too wondered: We grieved for the French soldiers, the Belgians, the Dutch. We feared for our men – would those caught be shot out of hand?

And Jean, so recently moved to the Dutch border with his regiment? Jean, with his great belief in the northern fortifications, the Maginot Line! "*On les aura, les Boche!*"

Reynaud's voice came through on the radio. There had been foul play. French officers, French officials, had betrayed French people. The northern fortifications had not been strong enough.

Then the dam burst. It had been under strain for many months. This was the start of a second wave of spy-mania. I was one of the first to be hit by it ...

Arriving back in Grau by bus (an infrequent summer bus-service from Agde had started), we found the inhabitants standing around in little clusters, whispering, following our movements with eager eyes, pointing at us. We were puzzled but shrugged off the strange behaviour of the locals. I felt sick. I was eager to get home.

As soon as we set foot in the place, police arrived. Our presence at the police-station was required. Bad news about Jean was my immediate thought. I had an urgent desire to faint, let myself collapse, but the greedy anticipation on the faces of the crowd wiped that thought from my mind.

At the police-station the Law of Grau was strutting up and down, banging the table, playing the leading role in a comic opera.

"It has been reported to me, ahem, ahem, that you are in radio contact with the enemy, ahem, ahem, that you lock yourself into your room for the purpose of these communications, that further, ahem, ahem, you meet strangers on the beach, indulge in long conversations with them, ahem, ahem. Can you explain your behaviour? ..."

I could! I did! Eddie could too. He did as well. The Law of Grau became downright rude. Eddie lost his temper. A shouting match started, and the relief to us both, Eddie and me, at being able to shout at someone, was tremendous.

Eve? Frustrated Eve, unable to engage sufficient attention for her laments about the 'little lamb', suspicious of my typewriter? And others of the grey whispering community? The Law of Grau retrieved its dignity with difficulty. I was released with a stern warning to mend my ways. After we arrived home, we shook with laughter but suddenly found ourselves holding on to each other shaking with tears. The policeman's antics had not wiped King Leopold's surrender off the slate. Then I went and was sick. I was surprised, for it seemed an unduly physical reaction!

Now the garrison was put on alert. The aliens of Grau, who were not on duty, clustered indoors around the radio. Avidly we waited for Reynaud's speeches. His news was always bad, but he did speak of fighting on, of 'dying for the cause'. We all wanted to fight on. We were all willing to die for the cause.

We formed an information centre around the radio during the days and nights of Dunkirk, wept with joy at the successful evacuation, with grief because we had not taken part. When Reynaud said that, if only a miracle could save France, he would believe in the miracle, that if they had to retreat as far as Africa, they would continue to fight from there, we believed that too, hoped for that miracle, were eager to join in the fight from Africa.

Then came the surrender of Paris!

Still we did not kiss our illusions good-bye. Again the roads overflowed with refugees. This time they all came: French families, French High Command, Czech High Command, Polish High Command, Czechs and Poles above military age, Americans – one huge stream struggling south, many hoping to reach Bordeaux and to sail on from there.

Our circle held on to its dreams. Arguments and discussions turned in never-ending circles around the next battles. Where would the regrouped Allied armies make their stand? Behind Paris? Would they build up a new front at the Loire? Time ran out on the dreams.

The *Marseillaise* was played, and Pétain announced that he had taken over the leadership of France.

The *Marseillaise* was played again, and Pétain announced that he had asked for an Armistice.

I cannot remember how it happened that we were all there, clustered around the radio, that no one had gone to camp. One of us shouted "No, no," as if he could stop the voice on the radio, could stop what was happening from happening. Several of us gasped ... then silence. The terrible silence. We sat numb.

Then I went and was sick. Since King Leopold's surrender, I had been sick with monotonous regularity. I felt that my body was letting me down and resented it.

My memory of the day of the Armistice is hazy. I think we all sat still for a long time. I remember hearing the *Marseillaise* and the announcement several times. Then someone suggested that we should bring guns out to Grau, to defend ourselves against the French, who were sure to run amok now. Everyone nodded agreement. Yes, that was a good idea! No one moved.

The *Marseillaise* came and went. Someone else suggested that we should pack a few things, walk towards the Spanish border, try to cross into Spain. Yes, that also was a good idea; everyone nodded and no one moved. A little later Eddie got up and said he would cycle into camp, to find out what was happening there. Of course! Swenska rose. He would go with him. They left.

The rest of us stayed. We were quite a crowd, for several Belgian officers had joined us. We listened to the *Marseillaise* and Pétain's speech hour after hour, as if the endless repetition would enable us to understand. It did not. We understood nothing.

7

Eddie and Swenska returned from Agde towards evening. They brought orders from the Czech CO for all Czechs to assemble at camp before midnight. The order extended to wives, children and parents; sick people were to be left behind. We would be evacuated the same night. One suitcase per person and hand-luggage, no more.

The crowd in the flat split up. What about the Belgian officers, we wondered, and looked at them with guilty faces. What would happen to them? I was obsessed by thoughts of my sister, Jean, the child. A wire had gone off to Feli two days earlier, asking her to come down south and join me.

It was a clear, starry night. Bright moonlight. A calm sea singing a calm eternal song. The sky and the sea had not changed.

The streets of Agde were alive with people streaming in. They had come from the surrounding camps, for Agde was the centre point. We stopped outside the camp gates, in front of the barbed wire, reluctant to go in before the appointed hour. We sat down on the edge of a ditch, quietly holding hands.

On the road, in front of us, a group had formed around a soldier, who declared, for everyone to hear, that he did not wish to be evacuated. He had lived for years in France. He was going to continue living in France, Germans or no Germans. He had friends who would hide him if need be. Hastily written letters were pressed into his hands, cables, money for stamps, money to pay for the cables.

I realized that I also did not want to be evacuated and leave my family behind. The thought of deserting them made me feel ill.

"Do we have to go?" I asked Eddie. "Can we not stay, hide

if necessary? What if Jean has been killed in Holland? If Feli is
left alone with the child?''

For a long while Eddie did not say anything. Nor did he let
go of my hand – we sat linked. Everything seemed strange,
unreal, our feet in the dry ditch, the rusty barbed wire behind
us, the velvety summer night, the milling crowds, the shouting
soldier; behind all that the knowledge of the collapse of France,
of impending evacuation. One could not cope, could not really
think.

After a while Eddie said in a low firm voice,

"I want to go. I want my chance to fight – I don't want to
hide.'' He did not look at me. He did not increase his hold on
my hand.

No, Eddie did not look at me. Someone else did. Thomas?
Clear brown eyes regarded me calmly, confidently, from a vast
distance. My whole being listened to those eyes. Can one
listen to eyes? I think one can. I did.

A little later I added my hastily scribbled letter and
centimes to the collection the soldier was holding. Then we
crossed over into camp.

It is after eleven when we arrive, and the camp is frantically
busy. Soldiers are running around, coping with orders and
counter-orders. Lorries draw up, are loaded with guns and
ammunition, blankets and iron rations, are driven off and
replaced by others. Margit and Swenska are waiting for us
behind the camp gates. Together with other women, Margit
and I are hustled into a room in the barracks, handed the
luggage, told to stay put and wait. Our men disappear. We
wait. We wait through the night. From time to time one or
other of our men looks in, brings some small thing which
might be useful now or on the journey. Chocolate. A mess-tin.
A water-bottle. We have been told to wear sensible clothes
and shoes suitable for long marches.

Sunrise finds us still at the camp, and the camp as busy as
ever. At eight o'clock orders come through to board the
lorries, boarding to proceed according to regiment and
company number. Dogs are to be left behind.

Margit and I board together. We put a blanket over our
part of bench and hide Tova beneath it. Tova seems to know

what is at stake: she lies motionless behind the blanket under the bench.

Again we wait. The sun is up, and it gets hot in the lorry. Tova's breathing becomes loud. I am worried that she will give her presence away, that she will suffocate.

At eleven o'clock we are ordered to dismount, collect our cases, form a queue. We stand in line by the lorry; lorries with their human tails cover the drill-ground. Around us officers and soldiers are moving like zombies.

We wait. It is noon, and the sun is hot. New orders come through over loudspeakers. We are to proceed to the officers' barracks; Lieutenant Thoren will guide us. We are to take our luggage with us.

The officers' barracks are about ten minutes away. We move slowly along with our cases, babies in arms, children clinging to their mothers' skirts. There are several dogs among us.

The officers' barracks are wooden huts, subdivided into small rooms, about fifty of them in all, standing opposite dilapidated stables. First-comers fill the rooms, the overflow sitting down in a dusty meadow next to the barracks in front of a horse-trough. We are about two hundred women plus children.

We wait. It is a relief to put down the luggage, to sit down oneself. I realize that I will not be able to walk very far with the amount of luggage I have: a rucksack, holding essentials, and my typewriter; gas mask and camera slung round my neck; two blankets, which Eddie has given me during the night, my lodencape and the suitcase. I am better-off than most of the women, certainly better-off than those with children! If I can hold on to the rucksack, typewriter, camera and lodencape on a walk of any length, I will be lucky!

A priest in the uniform of a second lieutenant appears. He is young and pale and seems very purposeful. He calls for the wives and children of soldiers to follow him. They are to come and collect some food at the main camp. The same ten minutes' walk. He says nothing about officers' wives. The priest and his flock march off.

Swenska comes around after a while. They are all hard at

work trying to organize the evacuation, he says. Permission for the early-morning lorries to leave camp has been refused by the French. He takes Margit to lunch – we are allowed an hour for lunch in town, and Eddie will call for me in a minute. Evacuation to where? Arranged by whom? The Czechs in France? In England? By the French? No one asks. No one even thinks the question.

Eddie arrives, and we go to Agde in search of something to eat. Cafés and restaurants are crowded; loudspeakers blare at us from every corner. Pétain speaks, and his voice echoes around the square, bounces at us from house after house. French officers and soldiers should follow him into the Armistice as they had followed their leaders before into war. And the *Marseillaise*. "*Le jour de gloire est arrivé.*" Everybody stands up, stands straight, takes off his hat, cap, beret.

And there it is again, this terrible sight, this heart-breaking sight that makes you wish to die. Hunched shoulders, lowered heads, strained faces, faces in which only the eyes are still alive, and, all alone, weep and weep.

They all cry, army personnel and civilians. They all cry, French and Allied officers. It does not matter which country's uniform they wear.

There must be some who are jubilant? They do not show themselves. Do they gloat behind closed shutters?

We choke on the food when we finally get it. On our way back to camp we say a quick 'Goodbye' to the *Veuve* Audouy. At camp Eddie disappears once more. I bring up all the food I had such trouble getting down, and Margit tells me to stay in the room and lie down. It might avoid an accident. What accident? I wonder. What is she talking about? My mind refuses to acknowledge that I might be with child. But I do lie down! I even fall asleep for a while, for I am tired out. Later I find the room intolerably hot and join the other women in the dusty meadow.

8

The soldiers' wives are back from their lunch. The afternoon is hot. We sit in the meadow. The children have started to run around and play. We wait. Waiting has already become part of our present life. Others make decisions for us, tell us what to do. It is a trap, an open invitation to stop thinking. Give in and take what is coming. This afternoon is the beginning. We are to have weeks of it.

I sit among the others, with Tova at my feet. A woman with a small white poodle in her arms sidles up to me. "You have a dog too," says the woman, "You will understand." She speaks in German in a high-pitched voice, her eyes wide open and staring.

"I've been told that we can't take dogs with us, that I will have to have mine destroyed," says the woman. "What are you going to do?"

What am I going to do? Take Tova with me, of course! There is no doubt in my mind at all.

"I will hide my dog under the lorry seat," I tell the woman.

"That's a clever idea," the woman says, pleased. "I will do the same."

She walks away with the poodle in her arms and tells everyone who will listen that this is what she is going to do. Gleefully she informs the priest, who is in charge of women and children, of her intention. The priest – much too young for the job they have given him – tells the woman that he cannot take her and the dog, and they walk away arguing.

"If you insist on keeping the dog," the priest says, "I will have to leave you behind."

Now the woman stops walking, stands still, screams that her fiancé is as good a Czech soldier as any other.

"He is at the front now. He cannot defend me. It is all the

fault of these beastly Jews," the woman shouts. She becomes
abusive. She is hysterical.

Another woman, who has been sitting quietly on the grass,
gets up, walks over to the screaming wretch, slaps her face.
The gesture, meant to stop the hysteria, is misunderstood by
the other women, who regard it as the signal for a fight. A
fight breaks out. It is the first of many. I sit on the dirty grass,
aghast, watching it. I wonder about my dreams of
comradeship, of helping each other to survive a common fate.
Two soldiers come running and help the priest to drag the
screaming woman away.

She comes back later. She seems very calm. Wrapped in this
majestic sort of calm, she announces loudly that they have put
her dog to sleep. She stands still among the women after her
announcement, watching them. Then she quietly sidles up to
a mother who is nursing a young baby and tells her that her
baby will have to be destroyed.

"If they destroy dogs," she says, "there is no reason why
babies should not be destroyed."

The mother bursts into tears. Other women lead the owner
of the poodle away, screaming and howling again. An officer
takes over. He takes her to the CO. The woman is not seen
again.

The priest is back. He is sliding through the ever-increasing
mass of women and children, trying to take down the names of
the women, their husbands, their children. He is trying to get
to know his flock. An impossible task.

At six o'clock orders come through again. "*Roskas!*" There
will be food for soldiers' wives and their children. Others have
permission to leave camp and go to town for dinner. Margit
and Swenska go to Agde for a meal. It is late by the time Eddie
arrives, and he is past any desire for food. He has spent the
day with his men under lorries, trying to get them
roadworthy. A wash and sleep is all he wants.

We get about two hours of sleep. At ten the barracks shake
with the return of people who had gone out and are now trying
to find a place to lie down. Stretchers are being rushed in, put
up in every available space. It becomes impossible to move. I
feel sick.

Camp stirs at 5 a.m., and shortly after six the gates are

closed. Are late-comers simply going to be left behind? They
had not been closed the day before. The women take the
closing of the gates as a sign that evacuation is imminent.

Eddie anticipates that he and I might be split up. We have
exchanged suitcases – his is the lighter one. The plan still
envisages a convoy of lorries with women and children in the
middle, soldiers and guns at either end.

"Don't worry, I'll see you before you leave. I'll be back
before anything happens."

The waiting begins again, the dust, the heat, the bickering,
but the morning is kept lively with announcements and orders
which seem to pour out of the loudspeakers. The first one is
more than welcome:

"*Roskas!* Women are to collect mess-tins and queue up for
coffee and bread."

Other orders follow:

"*Roskas!* All suitcases to be closed at once. Be ready to leave
at a moment's notice."

"*Roskas!* Queue up at the Red Cross tent for injections."

"*Roskas!* Assemble at point B for registration."

They lead nowhere. I come to the conclusion that the
function of orders not concerning food is to break up the
monotony of waiting and the tension which leads to unending
quarrels. At midday another order to queue up, tins in hand.
Soldiers bring huge dixies with soup and potatoes. In the
afternoon some mothers start a silent revolt, ignoring further
orders. The revolt spreads: it is unanimous. The loudspeakers
fall silent. The priest re-appears.

Rank of husband and religion are now added to his
questionnaire. Documents have to be handed over to bear out
individual statements. I am one of the first women he
approaches. I refuse to part with any of my papers. No papers,
no right to survive, no good. I will show them to him, yes; I
will not hand them over. News of my refusal spreads through
the women like wildfire. The priest retires defeated.

A little later another announcement over the loudspeakers:

"Only legally married women will get permission to leave
with the rest."

The order is not in line with Czech civil law, which
recognizes the 'common law' wife.

Margit's turn to become panic-stricken. Hedi also might be affected. We have lost contact with Hedi. Swenska comes racing up on a borrowed motorbike. A friend of his has whisked their papers from the CO's desk in Agde. He will take them to headquarters in Béziers, try to get permission through on the spot.

"Will there be time?"

"Yes, yes," says Swenska, "plenty of time, nothing will happen till tomorrow afternoon at the earliest."

Again women stand about in little groups, whispering to each other. Some crowd around Margit, try to calm her. New batches of refugees drift in – the priest brings a woman and her five-day-old baby into the room where I sit with Margit. The young mother, a pale, quiet slip of a girl, sits quietly in the room, the tiny bundle in her arms, a basket with nappies, bottle and tins of milk at her side. She does not smile. She does not talk. Her husband is at the front, the priest explains.

The priest keeps rushing in and out. The girl is in difficulties. A couple of hours after he has brought her, the priest fetches her away again. The girl carefully collects her nappies, bottles and tins of milk, packs them all back into the basket and leaves with the priest at her side. She looks heart-breakingly frail and vulnerable. The CO it appears, feels unable to take the responsibility for evacuating so young a child.

The women who have witnessed the scene stand in horror. Atrocity-stories immediately run riot. The Gestapo hold babies up by their feet and shoot them in the head in front of their mothers.

The speed with which rumours are born and handed around as fact puzzles me then and later. Where are they conceived? And why, dear God, why are they ever uttered? Rumours, the interminable waiting, the mindless, senseless orders which punctuate the waiting – a splendid recipe for creating hell.

Before the women can plumb the full depth of the atrocity-stories, they are interrupted by the sight of another woman, carried past them on a stretcher. She has been told that she too will not be allowed to go with the others; she will be left behind in France. Her husband has disobeyed orders. What orders? No one knows. The woman has fainted.

Margit, in a crumpled heap in a corner of the room, has been sitting thus since Swenska left. Usually so fastidious, she now looks dirty, dishevelled, her eyelids swollen from crying.

Orders! Only women and children to sleep in the officers' barracks. The men can sleep at the main camp. Ready for evacuation at 7 a.m. Anybody who wants to, can leave for the night.

Eddie arrives shortly after six. He has seen some of the landladies from Agde at the camp gates, he says. We wait till eight for Swenska's return from Béziers and take our blankets with us when we leave. Tonight we will bed down in the open.

Rose is standing in front of the camp gates. She arrived with other women at five. She heaves a sigh of relief and says: "*Voilà – enfin!* Maman wants you to come home. She is waiting with supper for you."

"*Alors, ça y est? On s'en va?*" she adds impatiently, as Eddie and I stand still and stare at her. We do not say anything. Rose prattles on as we walk along, we do not hear what she says.

"*A la maison,*" the *Veuve* Audouy also says: "*Voilà! Enfin!*" Two places are laid for us on the kitchen table. The widow is busy with pots and pans.

"Would you like a wash before supper?"

It seems as if having supper in the kitchen of *La Veuve* Audouy is a daily event for us, for which, today, we are a bit late.

"It is important to eat well in times of stress." states the widow when we come down from the washroom. "Keep body and soul together."

She does not say anything when I have to rush out in the middle of her lovely meal. When I come back, she excuses herself and leaves the kitchen. We will spend the night with her, she announces on her return; she has just moved the French officers together into the room they used to share. "It won't hurt them for a few days!" After supper I am sent unceremoniously to bed. Eddie, the widow suggests, might like to smoke a last cigarette in the garden?

She times her entrance to perfection. I have just hopped into bed. A knock, and she is there, closes the door carefully

behind her, sits down at the edge of the bed and takes my
hand.

"*Alors, ma petite, ça y est.*"

It is not a question but a statement, and I want to tell her
that I'm not sure at all. I do not get a chance.

Not an ideal start for a baby, no certainly not, she says, but
never mind, we can't always choose.

"*Du courage, surtout, du courage!*"

One has to be practical, to think carefully. No carrying of
suitcases or other heavy things.

"Things," she says full of contempt. "One can buy again.
Not a baby." Warm clothes, yes, that is important.

"Try not to catch cold. Tie them round your neck if you
can't carry them. God knows where they are taking you to.
Don't stand any more than you have to. There is always a
floor to sit on or God's good earth. And keep yourself regular,
that is important. Buy some medicine tomorrow in Agde. No,
I will buy it in case you are not allowed out. Rose will bring it
to you. Food, well, it might be difficult. The baby will take
what it needs. You are young. Keep your head. No
unnecessary efforts. And courage, most of all, never lose
courage. God be with you."

She kisses me on the forehead and very quickly goes out of
the room, her long black skirt swirling and rustling.

I sit up in bed and stare after her. Long after she has gone I
stare at the door through which she left.

It seems to me that the *Veuve* Audouy, that tall, beautiful
woman from the *Ville Noire* of Agde has just made it possible
for me to have my child. If there is a child. If, at this moment
in time, I am meant to carry that most precious gift: a new life.

God be with her, now and for evermore, I think. And with
those of her ilk.

Margit seems more hopeful when we see her again.
Swenska, she says, has been successful in Béziers. He has
received verbal permission; written permission for their
marriage is to follow.

The third day in camp. An order booms from the
loudspeakers:

"Women in the last months of pregnancy are to join a

special unit. Any woman more than six full months pregnant is to report ..."

All the women in camp unite. Mothers stop their eternal washing at the horse-trough and join the others. The medical team which has come to lead the pregnant women away is faced with a suspicious, hostile crowd. What happened to the frail young girl with her five-day-old baby is not going to be repeated without a fight!

We are convinced that these women also are going to be left behind. Two days ago we all trooped into camp like sheep, full of confidence. Forty-eight hours later we are suspicious. The CO might refuse to take responsibility for these women as well, and we are not going to let that happen.

It is a perfectly sensible order. There is one woman among us, just going into her seventh month of pregnancy, who looks desperately ill. Another, who says she has four weeks to go, looks like coming down any moment. Of course they need extra care.

The medical team calms our suspicions, reassuring the 'special cases'. They are led away to the Red Cross tent.

Eddie comes early for lunch. I search his face for some news, but he shakes his head.

"The French are delaying the evacuation," he says. "They are demanding a full account of every item put at the disposal of the Czech Legion, down to empty shell-cases."

He looks tired. His face is drawn. Sweat and dust have crept into every line and make an exaggerated mask out of the tired features. On a sudden impulse he has cycled to Grau at four in the morning to collect what might become possible means of survival for us in the distant future: engineering patents, scripts. We will leave them with Madame Audouy.

Special guards are on duty when the camp is invaded in the afternoon by a wave of black-clad women. They arrived at five and waited a while outside the gates. It is five-thirty now, and they are coming in. They push arms, bayonets, pointed rifles out of their way, ignore shouting soldiers and shouting officers, roll on.

They find the women's camp and with cries of joy spread themselves over it, discover former tenants and greet them like

long lost relatives. Some women who have come in from
Béziers and other Czech army camps find themselves
suddenly pulled up by a Frenchwoman whom they have never
seen before. The words "*A la maison!*" go up like a battlecry.
Now each Agatoise has at least one Czech woman by the hand
and triumphantly marches her past the officers who have
stopped running and shouting, past the guards who have at
last closed their gaping mouths.

Rose is among the folk from Agde and has me firmly by the
hand. Luckily Eddie came back early this afternoon: we do
not have to leave a message for him.

The picture of that group of black-clad women, spreading
themselves over the camp, unafraid of rifles and bayonets,
ignoring shouts and commands, motivated by compassion,
has stayed with me. I carry a flag for the women of Agde!

Descendants of pirates? If that is what it does for you, I wish
the entire world were populated with the descendants of
pirates.

A telegram is waiting for me at the house of the *Veuve*
Audouy. It is from Feli. It says: "Unable to join you. Good
luck. God bless."

It comes from Clermont Ferrand.

It does not say if Jean is alive, dead or a prisoner of war. For
two years I was to know no more about my family; not till they
escaped to Algiers did I learn that they were together and safe.

9

On the sixth day after the Armistice, camp starts moving.

Nothing much has distinguished the last days from the first. The men have been asked to decide individually whether to stay in France or leave with the remnants of the Czech Legion. Those who decide to stay will be given French papers. Those who decide to leave must swear a new oath of allegiance, pledge themselves to fight on.

Beneš, we are told, has spoken on the radio. From England. He will do what he can for us, the Czechs in France.

Beneš is far away. England is even further, unreal. Real is the camp, the dust, the heat, the squabbles and the hysterics, the tears. Real is the waiting: it is a totally absorbing, totally exhausting occupation. Real are the advancing Germans with their threat of the Gestapo, but even that has lost its edge. Fear also has dulled. The waiting saps all, hope and fear alike.

Margit and Swenska have heard nothing further from Béziers. Their papers have not been returned. Swenska is still optimistic – headquarters promised! Margit is not sure. They have found a room in Grau for the nights and borrow our bikes for the journeys.

The generosity of the women of Agde has become an embarrassment. They will not accept pay. They insist on the nightly return of their visitors. Rose waits at the camp gates every evening. I become nervous at the thought of keeping her waiting. The French officer, whose room we occupy, is hostile. He is of the opinion that if they, the French, cannot get out, there is no reason for the Czechs to be given permission to leave the country. Threat of the Gestapo to serving Czech soldiers and their families? A Free French force outside France? "*Quelle bêtise!*" Eddie and I dare not say much for fear of embarrassing our host.

On the sixth day lorries drive up to the women's camp, and soldiers jump down, demanding all luggage. One case per woman, the minimum of hand-luggage only. After the long inactivity there is a sudden urgency, which quickly leads to panic. The soldiers become abusive, the women hysterical. I get involved in a fight with a soldier about my typewriter. It is a stupid fight.

For six days now I have carted my typewriter and my camera around with me. As long as I have those, we will not starve, I will be able to earn money. It is a portable, with a solid lid. It does look like a small case. I cannot explain what it is to the soldier who speaks only Czech. In the middle of hurry, confusion and sharp words, I demonstrate the typewriter to him. I win that fight.

A small woman standing next to me has no suitcase at all but a huge bundle knotted into one sheet and slung over her shoulder. She has a child of about two, whom she usually carries, and a boy of perhaps six, who holds on to her skirt. She arrived two days ago from Belgium, speaking only French. She does not know what happened to her husband; her brother has been killed; her mother has died of a heart-attack – all within the first day of the German attack. She has walked with the two children long stretches of the road south. Quietly and tearlessly she now fights for her bundle of bedding and will not let go.

The soldier tears it out of her arms. The woman stands speechless and bereft, staring at the soldier, the two children beside her. The noisy collection of luggage goes on, and still the woman stands motionless. It seems to me that she is in shock, that something dreadful will happen to her if she is just left like that. I take her in my arms. I hold her tight for I don't know how long. Slowly I can feel the terrible tension leave her body. Such a small thin body, I wonder how she has had the strength to walk that long way south, carrying the child. Her name, she says, is Renée.

My turn for heartbreak. Tova. The fight that I am going to lose. The fight I am not even able to fight.

We have sat down again, after the soldiers and their lorries have left, still on that ever more dirty bit of ground in front of the officers' barracks. From far away I see Sergeant Welzek approaching. He is inexorably marching towards me from the rim of the world. I have been expecting him. I have been dreading his arrival. Since the appearance of the lorries earlier on I have known that he will come today.

There is something terrible about an unavoidable 'NOW' like that. Even if you have already lived through it so many times in your mind that you pray for it to happen and be over with. Now!

I watch Sergeant Welzek approaching. Every step he takes toward me is taking place inside me and hurts physically.

After five full days at camp it is quite impossible for me to smuggle Tova out. Everyone has seen her. Everyone knows about her. Eddie has said that he will try to take her with him. I have clung to that hope. It is not a real hope.

If he cannot take her with him, he will shoot her, Eddie has promised. Death in preference to suffering.

Welzek has reached me. He salutes. He holds out his hand. He does not say anything. What is there to say? I hand him Tova's lead. He marches off. Tova trots beside him. A very obedient dog. She goes without a struggle.

Her four legs move forward. Her head is turned backward. Her eyes do not leave me. My eyes do not leave her. As long as we can still see each other ...

I can still see her. Her paws set up little clouds of dust. Head turned backwards, ears pricked up. Waiting for a call? A whistle? That picture will stay with me to the end of my days and lose none of its agony. I am walking with her.

She is going towards her death. Mine as well. The death of all I have been, all I have known, before the outbreak of that war.

At the time I was ashamed of the utter agony I felt. So many women around me had lost so much more.

I am not ashamed of it now.

It was early afternoon when the order came through to form an orderly line of two by two, ready for evacuation. The soldiers had left with their lorries at about 10 a.m. Welzek came soon afterwards. Since Welzek left I had been waiting to hear a shot. I had not heard it. My mind wandered. I was worried about Margit, who was not back from Béziers. Margit and Swenska had left in a panic in the early morning to retrieve their papers. Headquarters, so they were told, had packed up and left.

The column of women and children marching back to the main camp was long, slow and untidy, full of mothers terrified of losing their straying, lagging children. Red Cross vans were waiting for us at the main camp. The sight of the Red Cross surprised us. The women were pushed into the vans without ceremony, six adults per van regardless of the number of their children. The last woman in was handed iron rations for the lot, milk for the children, hard-boiled eggs, cheese and biscuits. She was now in charge.

My turn. I hesitated, someone was grabbing my elbow, shoving me roughly into the nearest van. I was fighting back, looked up indignantly and saw that it was Eddie.

"Stay in that van," he said, "you must stay in that van. I'll join you in Sète."

"In Sète?"

"Yes, in Sète. We are boarding ships in Sète."

"Ships?" My face was blank. I did not comprehend.

"Ships," Eddie repeated patiently. "Yes, I will join you. Yes, I promise. Stay in the van. Don't get out till you are told to."

He handed me a thermos flask, then he disappeared, and I could hear him speak to the driver in Czech.

"The driver will take care of you," he shouted into the van, just before the door was being closed.

I meant to ask him about Tova, but he had already moved away, and the closing door slammed the words back at me.

No windows in the van, a ventilation grill only. Claustrophobic! The vehicles stood in the sun, motionless, till loading was completed. It was just over an hour to Sète, but it seemed much longer. Arrived, they stopped and stood, doors still locked, the temperature soaring once more. When a child started screaming, the mother hammered at the locked door. After a few moments the driver opened the door, and the woman persuaded him to keep it open. He stood guard in front of it. Now we could hear the hammering from other vans, still locked, and see several with their doors open already.

When we were at last let out, we found ourselves at a

quayside. Once more we had to form a queue and were marched in twos towards a small dark-looking ship, flying the French tricolour. Our luggage was lined up along the quay. We were ordered to collect our cases. One narrow gangway connected the ship to the quay, allowing one person at a time to cross it. Two officers were standing on either side, and again all papers were checked. No cursory check, this! One by one the women were released across the gangway, carrying their goods, pushing their children in front of them, dragging them after themselves. Babies were handed around like boxes of sweets, crying with terror at the many unfamiliar hands. On the other side of the gangway the fatherless families assembled again, walked round a corner on the ship and disappeared from sight. The ship seemed to swallow them up.

I was standing in the middle of the long queue. I had remembered the advice of the *Veuve* Audouy and put my case down, but there was no chance to sit down, for the queue was moving, if only inch by inch. I was burdened by my possessions: blankets and lodencape, camera and typewriter, rucksack, gasmask, suitcase. I was struggling with an intense desire to break rank and run for it. My eyes were scouting for a place to run to. Eddie arrived at the crucial moment, jumped out of a jeep and ran towards me. No, he was not going aboard with me; his task was not finished; he would board during the night. No, I could not wait for him; I would not get a second chance, for women and children had to board now. NOW! He had only come to make sure that I would go aboard, to see me onto the ship.

"If we get separated, we will communicate via Hans and Helen in America."

"Wait four weeks before contacting the Red Cross, before taking official steps, before giving in to despair."

As if one could schedule despair! It was with us. Eddie, at my side, did not speak any more. He seemed unapproachable, adamant.

Dumb with horror I watched the last three women in front of me disappear. I was desperate to stop time, prevent from happening what was so unavoidably going to happen. I stumbled past control and onto the gangway. I recognized

Renée, the little woman from Belgium, standing on the ship and holding out her hand to me, and I wondered why she was doing this. Someone behind me said,

"Careful of the step. God bless you," and I turned round, surprised. I saw Eddie's face.

If you have lived a moment like that, it leaves you with the prayer that you might never have to live another one like it, that you might be spared that sort of agony on anyone's face for evermore.

10

It was the starboard hold into which women and children had disappeared. A tarpaulin covered it, a lamp swinging from the middle. Once I got accustomed to the dim light, I could make out a mass of figures sitting on straw.

"Sit down, sit down, find yourself a place, make yourself as comfortable as you can," voices shouted out in different languages. Again the priest glided in and out among the huddled figures; although in uniform, he always seemed to glide.

The hold was overcrowded by the time the last women from the quayside had been absorbed, Margit among them. She and Swenska had not been able to retrieve their papers in Béziers. Headquarters had gone. I asked Margit to safeguard 'my place', scrambled on deck, rushed to the ship's rails. Eddie might still be around. No! Of course not. I watched military kitchens being brought aboard with difficulties. It started to rain. Uniformed men shouted at me. I climbed down into the hold again.

Women were distributing food, biscuits, cheese, hard-boiled eggs, milk for the children. The priest announced that the pregnant women had been brought aboard and were housed in cabins. Blankets were handed to those who had none. Night was coming.

Under cover of darkness Margit and I crept back on deck. It was still raining. Sheltered under one of the lifeboats, we watched the embarkation of soldiers, trying to recognize faces, figures, movements. Towards dawn Margit spotted her fiancé and went to him. I stayed on deck.

At daylight I tried to find out from the soldiers if Eddie was aboard. He might have boarded while I was not looking, I might have missed seeing him in the dark. "*Nadporucik*

Deichsler? *Nadporucik* Deichsler?'' He was not aboard. He had promised to come, but he had not come.

Soldiers, officers, shouted at me to get off the deck, waved their arms about, opened their mouths wide. I saw rather than heard their shouts. Why should I leave the deck? I did not ask. They did not explain. I meekly followed their orders. The process of dehumanization is fast. I was conscious of being dirty, unkempt, disgusting with my frequent bouts of sickness. I had no rights.

During the day we were allowed on deck for one purpose only.

Soldiers guarded the single access, an iron ladder; the hazardous journey up was followed by a long wait. A queue stretched halfway round the deck. The queue also was guarded by soldiers. Many women gave up. Mothers had to give up. There was straw. The hold was being turned into a stable.

Time lost all meaning. I was numb, comatose. People trod on me, stepped over me. I saw what was going on without registering it. It seemed to be happening in a different world, in a far-away chamber of horrors. Margit twice forced me to come to. She and two other women were called away. She alone came back, in tears. There was still trouble about her missing papers. She was not sure that she would be allowed to come with us. Swenska again had taken up the fight, had gone back to Agde, she said. Eddie was still working flat out. Transport for the soldiers returning from the north had priority.

Food was distributed at intervals, no drink, except the milk for the children. Thermos-flasks and water-bottles ran out. The women complained about hunger and thirst; children whimpered. The dim light in the hold made little division between day and night. At some point I noticed that Margit was no longer at my side. Someone said she had been called away again.

During a short moment of awareness I heard the priest calling for silence. We would have to disembark, he announced. The captain of the French ship had refused to put out to sea with us on board, since his ship was not adequately equipped. He had never agreed to take women and children.

I was among the first ones out! We had been forty-five hours on that ship, but it seemed longer. We were ordered to pick up our luggage, still standing on deck, and form the usual two-by-two line on the quayside. We stood for hours. The line moved only sufficiently to absorb disembarking women. I thought about the advice of the *Veuve* Audouy, but we were not allowed to sit on our cases, much less on the ground. It made counting difficult! We were continually counted, surrounded by guards and military police.

The sun was merciless, that end of June in the South of France. I wished that I had a hat, sun-glasses. You do not think of taking a straw hat and sun-glasses when you are told to take warm clothes and stout shoes. I thought of the *Veuve* Audouy and wondered what I could discard. The case? That would be noticeable, create suspicion. The blankets? The blankets. I had the lodencape. It would do.

It took me long to reach that decision. We all stood patiently, resigned, like cattle. I folded one blanket up, made as small a parcel as I could and shoved it aside with my foot. Slowly, slowly, we moved away from it. The little parcel was one yard, two yards, three yards behind me. When I judged it at a safe distance, I repeated the process with the second blanket. When that was at a safe distance, I started thinking about the case again. We were being marched off before I could come to a decision.

We were marched along the harbour, past several groups of women. I spotted Margit in one of the groups, moved towards her and was pushed back harshly. Military police! I refrained from going berserk, shouted to Margit and was told to shut up. French military police! I let fly with every French swear word I could think of. The man smiled. Perhaps he had not expected such fluency.

"*Alors!* D'you want to be evacuated or not?"

I said, "Not really."

The chap looked at me, not smiling any more. I noticed that Margit had heard me and was following us, and the other women followed her.

In the distance we saw a big ship. It flew the British flag. We looked at it full of envy. Lucky ship, it could be in England in a few hours' time, the England of Dunkirk. We looked further afield to see what other ships there were.

Our long column was halted at the first gangway leading up to the British ship. The chattering in front and behind me grew louder. A strange experience, this, communal silence, little whispers floating along like a gentle breeze, subdued sounds full of excitement, suddenly a crescendo sweeping over you. A voice cut sternly into the babble: "*Roskas!*" We were to board the ship, one by one. Cases to be left on deck.

No check on papers this time. Czech officers at the bottom of the gangway, English naval officers on deck. The English officers smiled at us as we came up the gangway. "Welcome aboard!" they said.

Welcome aboard? To a heap of dirty unkempt women, jetsam of this war, unnecessary, burdensome strangers? Welcome aboard! Someone took my case out of my hand. A police voice asked me in English to follow him. Without a question-mark in my mind, I followed. That voice could have led me anywhere.

It led me to a cabin. The English crew had put their cabins at our disposal. It was a small cabin – narrow bunkbed, seat, washstand. It seemed beautiful to me. Behind me a high-pitched voice said: "*C'est magnifique.*" A fat young woman with pitch-black hair and olive skin had followed me in. I had never seen her before.

The owner of the English voice turned around. He was tall, sunburned, immaculate, friendly. Would we like some whisky? No? Cigarettes? He held out his packet to us.

"Put your things down," he said. "Don't worry, nobody will chase you out of here. This is my cabin. I can do what I like with it."

It sounded immensely unlikely. We gratefully accepted a cigarette each. He gave us the packet and left. I put my belongings on the bunkbed, and the dark-haired girl spread hers over the seat. We lit the cigarettes, watching the smoke fill the little cabin. The girl said she came from Morocco. Czech pilots had been stationed in Morocco.

Later we were called on deck. It was evening and bitter cold, and we all shivered. Once again we were welcomed aboard by the English crew, were handed more cigarettes. And tea! Hot tea – beautiful!

Plenty of British ships were calling at French ports in the south, one crew-member assured me when I asked. "We have orders to enter ports and pick up everyone who wants to go."

Eddie would have a chance. If he could get himself to a port, he would have a chance. I tried to reach him in my mind. I tried to will him to a port.

Five more women were in the cabin when we got back, a Czech officer with them. Each cabin had to take seven women, he said, two on the bunk, two on the chair, three on the floor.

I shared the bunk with a girl from Hungary. She spoke Hungarian and French, and the girl from Morocco spoke French only, so we settled on French as the language. The Moroccan girl was in sole possession of the seat, for it was too small to be shared. Port-holes had to be closed. We left the door open to get air, but so many people trod on the four women on the floor that we shut it.

In the morning, when I wanted to change my shirt, I discovered that the cases had gone. Some had been lowered into the holds, others thrown overboard. A thousand troops had boarded during the night, picked up on the road south – another five hundred were still boarding.

Hot tea and cigarettes, provided by the crew, gave a temporary respite, but a glance over the ship's rail onto the quay – and one was back in the nightmare. Groups of pale, distraught people were standing there, Margit and Hedi among them. They had spent the night on the pier, frightened to let the ship out of their sight because this coal-ship, the *Northmoor*, was the only one ordered to take the contingent of Czech women and children. We anxiously watched every move of Margit and Hedi. We saw them walking away with one officer, come back with a group of officers, purposefully march up to the Czech CO.

By their gestures we could see that a lively discussion followed, in which Hedi took no part. We saw her looking towards us and edging away from the group, watching them till she was perhaps ten yards apart. Then she turned around, ran towards a rope-ladder which was hanging down from our side of the ship and started climbing it.

Margit spotted her absence, looked up, saw her, hesitated a moment and also made a dash towards the ladder. She had

reached the bottom rung, Hedi halfway up, when the officers'
group broke apart and all of them ran towards the two girls.

Hedi was quick. She was pulled aboard by many hands
before the officers had reached the ladder. Margit was on the
bottom rung but out of reach. She was slow, clumsy. Among
the shouting officers was Swenska. He yelled at her to come
down again. We shouted at her to continue climbing, holding
out our hands towards her. No! Margit played the game by
the rules. She went down.

Later I saw her sitting on the edge of the pier. She was
sobbing. She had been finally refused, she said. There was no
more chance. She had no papers. They had disappeared with
the files at the headquarters in Béziers. Only her French
identity-card was left to her. Why had she not climbed aboard
like Hedi? Swenska had not wanted her to. He had thought he
would be able to get her aboard legally. I felt suspicious about
Swenska's motives. I wondered what came first in his mind,
Margit or his army career.

I stayed near the rail, and Margit sat hunched on a bollard
on the pier. There was not much more we could say to each
other. A little while later we watched a woman climbing down
the rope ladder – the gangways were guarded at both ends.
She had a paper in her hand. A letter from the ship's captain,
a woman told me – there was always somebody who knew it
all – giving her written permission to bring her parents
aboard. The English captain had written a note to the Czech
CO making himself responsible for the two elderly people.

The Czech CO tore the letter up and let the pieces flutter
away.

The woman collapsed. Her parents, small, grey, late fifties,
turned towards each other, sobbing on each other's shoulders.
They had been standing apart from the others. They looked
pathetically alone, forlorn.

Two soldiers hooked their arms under the woman's armpits
and dragged her back on board like a drunk. First her heels
clattered over the cobbled stone of the pier, then she lost a
shoe.

An English voice next to me said: "We don't treat dogs like
that in England ..." A crew-member. I had not noticed him
before. He had not spoken to me, he had spoken to himself. I

looked at him, and he blushed. He was very young, untouched. Blessed – there was a whole country behind him!

I tried to find an answer to his remark. I could not find one. There was no answer.

Suddenly it all seemed too much, much too much to be borne. I was seized by the desire to rush to the other side of the ship and jump overboard. Out of life.

I was no longer entitled to my dreams of escape! The realization came as a shock. I had more to lose than myself: another life depended on mine. It had all the priorities. It had all the rights. The time had come to be sure. I did feel sure. At that precise moment I felt convinced that I was with child.

It made me feel ten feet high. My spirit soared. All the fear I had been burdened with fell away from me. Of course I had been afraid, we had all been afraid, but I was afraid no longer. I was strong. If need be, I could move mountains.

When I took note of my surroundings again, I noticed that they had rolled up the rope ladder. I saw two soldiers rushing a stretcher up the gangway. Immediately after them both gangways were pulled up. The ship's engines had been going since early morning. She was making ready to sail.

Margit, down on the pier, saw the preparations and sat up.

The ship moved. Slowly it carried out its first manoeuvres. Already there was a gap of several yards between us and the pier, between us and the Continent.

Margit rose, standing as if turned to stone. She watched the ship. I watched her. Her face seemed frozen in horror and disbelief. Within seconds I could no longer make out her features.

I saw her throw her arms into the air. She screamed. The gap between us grew larger and larger, but her scream followed the ship like a seagull. Her scream hit me. Perhaps I screamed as well. I do not know. I blacked out.

That was the last I saw of the Continent: Margit, with her arms thrown into the air, standing at the edge of the shrinking pier.

When I came to, there was just a coastline, and from where I lay it looked as if it were being crossed out by the ship's rails.

11

"*Elle est avec moi. Elle est avec moi,*" I heard a high-pitched voice say, realized that the voice was referring to me and wondered what Eliane, the Moroccan girl, was talking about. I was not with anyone. I was on my own.

"*Dans la cabine,*" the voice was pleading. Eliane looked down on me, her dark eyes soft as velvet. I walked back to the cabin with her and Imogen, our young Hungarian mate. Was Margit still screaming, I wondered?

"Lie down – *couchez vous,*" and, as I resisted: "*Mais soyez raisonable!*"

It seemed an unjustifiable request at that moment. Then I remembered that there might be justification for it.

I lay down. My flesh shrank in anticipation of the insects which inhabited the wooden bunk, but I lay still. The women left the cabin. Eliane reassuringly patted my shoulder before she went out. The cabin was empty.

I tried to think away from what had happened, think instead of what might be: the log cabin in the woods, the boy with the laughing brown eyes, full of life. No! Too far away. Dreams of another time.

But then I did feel eyes on me, calm, unblinking eyes, bridging the distance. I was not alone. It would be all right, said the eyes. It would all be all right.

The cabin did not remain empty. Women kept popping in, their voices loud, their gestures excited. A Czech woman, who had been put in charge of a Red Cross van, was the first.

"Have you seen Hedi?" she asked in a harsh, officious voice, her eyes searching the cabin.

Where in that cabin would I hide Hedi? Suddenly I was

convinced that under the thin veneer of a Czech soldier's wife hid a *Gauleiter*.

Her fair hair was pulled back from face and forehead as if every stray hair risked the death sentence. Her movements were abrupt, without grace or femininity. A *Gauleiter*! I had not seen Hedi since many hands had helped her aboard. I would not have told the *Gauleiter* if I had. What was she going to do with the girl if she did find her? Throw her overboard?

The *Gauleiter* left. Eliane returned together with Imogen. "*Ça va mieux?*" They nodded approvingly, satisfied with my behaviour. Sensible! They began to busy themselves at the washbasin, played about with the taps, chattered, waited, tried the taps again. No water, they said in great astonishment. An elderly woman marched in, knocking them flat against the wall, closely followed by her daughter. Both women lined up in front of the bunk, drowning me with Czech words.

"What do they want?" I asked the Hungarian girl.

"She is a colonel's wife and thinks her rank entitles her to the bunk."

"She can have the bunk."

"Speak Czech. We are all Czechs, aren't we?" said the colonel's wife.

"They are going to see the CO. They want a cabin for themselves," translated Imogen.

The colonel's wife and daughter marched out. The two girls tried the taps again, repeated: "*Il n'y a pas d'eau ...*" and also disappeared. "*A toute à l'heure.*"

The *Gauleiter* returned.

"There is no water on board this ship," she announced joyfully, speaking German without reluctance.

She came back later – she was incredibly busy, that woman. "There is no food on board," she said. "Military kitchens and provisions have been left aboard the French ship." It sounded as if she was announcing a great victory.

"I have some bread and cheese left, would you like some?"

Was she trying to be friendly? Or had she been carefully husbanding her means of power? How could she have anything left of the little given to her after that length of time?

I could not pursue the subject. The toilets, where were the toilets? But that was the moment when the cabin was empty, the corridor outside the cabin empty, no one to be seen.

"Only one toilet for women and children," a woman I finally located announced proudly.

Later, on the crowded deck, another woman impassively confirmed the disagreeable news. Military kitchens and the bulk of the provisions had been left aboard the French ship. Troops had boarded the *Northmoor* during the night. Each soldier on arrival had had a quick drink and a wash. No one had noticed it or tried to stop them. The water-shortage had been discovered after we left harbour. Water would be rationed. Toilets? There were five, as far as she knew. "One for the crew, one for the Czech top-brass, one for the other officers, one for the troops, one for us." She was counting them off on her fingers, and it was right, it did come to five. How many top-brass did we have on board then? How many officers in all? Fifteen hundred troops? About three hundred women and children? I did not ask. Did anybody really know? Some time later it started to rain, beautiful soft rain. One could still see the coastline, far away now! A Czech officer walked by and imperiously ordered us off deck.

The return to the cabin brought the return of the sickness problem.

The women were smoking. The cabin immediately became stuffy. I thought that there must be an answer to that recurring difficulty. The crowded deck was no solution. I felt full of envy for women who were able to be sick without worry, who had 'facilities' at hand. Did they realize how lucky they were? I decided to queue up now, in time, since standing in the passage could not be worse than sitting in the cabin!

It was worse. By the time I discovered it, I was built into the queue.

An officer walked by. He was moving past so quickly that I nearly missed him, but I recognized him, having met him several times at the dinner-dances. He was a doctor who had had a fashionable practice in Karlsbad – he might help! I broke out of the queue, abandoning the hard-earned progress. The doctor greeted me effusively. Could he give me something against nausea, please?

He was very suave, very superior. He put a hand on my shoulder and said in well-timbred tones: "It is all a question of self-control." I stared at him full of dislike, and he looked at me with cold, contemptuous eyes.

The short encounter had distracted my attention from the job in hand, and now it was too late. I had just time to mumble: "Pregnant", turn away from him. No self-control! One of these inferior beings! Decent people are not pregnant at moments like this. The doctor from Karlsbad no longer spoke to me. He waved to an orderly, commanded crisply: "Take her to the upper deck and put her down there somewhere." He marched purposefully away.

The orderly was kind. He insisted that I should have a blanket in addition to the lodencape, and fetched one.

"Not to worry," he said, "Got a wife myself and two kiddies, know all about it."

He made a bed out of ship's hawser and canvas, and when he gently and caringly spread the blanket over me, added:

"Wonder where they'll land us? Morocco, maybe? I'd like that. Got my family there. Or Oran? Don't worry about a thing now, I'll wake you in plenty of time. You just sleep."

Where we would land? We had only just left! I had forgotten that we would have to land somewhere, sometime. Where? All of us? Even if Eddie managed to get away, would we be landed within reach of each other? Would I ever see him again?

The rain was soft. I hugged my child in my mind.

The night started badly. The orderly was late, he had not known, he said, that curfew for women and children was at 7 p.m. None of his comrades had come across Lieutenant Deichsler from Brno. There had been trouble with the lorries! We rushed towards the cabin.

I had missed whatever had been offered in the way of food and drink. Why did we have to be in the cabin by seven? No one knew. No one queried it. *Roskas!*

I was the last one in. The women had waited for me before settling. The colonel's wife and daughter sat militantly on the bunk. Eliane was spread over her stool. The four of us who were left arranged ourselves on the floor, I with my head against the door. I was happy about that arrangement: if need be, I would be able to get out or open the door a fraction if it got too hot and stuffy inside.

Around midnight I opened the door slightly. The smell of hot engine-oil poured into the cabin immediately, the noise of the engine hammering it home. I had to get out. Outside in the gangway a sentry pointed his gun at me. Let him shoot!

There was no queue outside the toilet. There was a 'courting' couple inside it. Later on, I found an iron ladder along the passageway, leading to the small upper deck, where I had been in the afternoon. The deck was strewn with sleeping figures wrapped in coats and blankets. I joined them, hiding in my cape. It was still raining, a fine, drizzly summer rain. I woke frequently. At the first sign of dawn I crept down the iron ladder. There was a chest standing next to the bottom rung, still in the open ... I curled up on top of it and slept till someone woke me, calling my name.

It was a friendly guard who knew me from Agde.

"*Inspektion*," he said urgently. "*Kabine. Inspektion.*" He pointed to the cabin.

No, not the cabin. I sat down on the floor outside the cabin, leaning against the door, guarded by the sentry and his gun.

12

On the second full day aboard the *Northmoor*, orders once again jubilantly took off. Our CO had recovered his impetus. The loudspeakers spewed forth a never-ending stream.

Like the hare in Aesop's fables, you never made the queues you were ordered to attend in time.

"*Roskas!* Queue up on points A and B at 7 a.m. Tea will be distributed by courtesy of the ship's crew."

That one no one missed out on, and the crew kept it up for the whole of our time on the *Northmoor*, a mug of tea morning and night. With sugar. Did they guess how much it meant to us?

"*Roskas!* Rations are to be drawn at eight."

And at 1 p.m., and at 6 p.m. The rations were a memory of food rather than food. That there were any rations for women was something to be grateful for. A spoonful of rice, or soup, a biscuit, a piece of dry bread: we were painfully hungry, but not starving. The energy required for standing in the queue was not in proportion to the prize obtained; nevertheless, you queued. You were not allowed to draw rations for anyone but yourself and your children. If you did not want to queue for your rations, you were allowed to be as hungry as you liked.

"*Roskas!* Mess-tins are now to be washed out with salt water at point X."

"*Roskas!* Women with children to queue at starboard, women without children at portside, to give their particulars to the officers in charge at the two points."

Place and date of birth. Religion. Mother-tongue! Nationality before marriage.

"*Roskas!* Taps will now be turned on for one hour. The ration is one mug per person. Queue up on – "

Taps were turned on twice a day, mid-morning and mid-afternoon. There were two of them. It took longer than one hour to work through the queue. Someone always went without water. The water-queue was predestined to become a battleground with its daily quota of losers, an open invitation to hostility and panic.

"*Roskas!* Queue up at 2 p.m. Bring your papers to substantiate your statements of this morning."

I wondered how Renée was. Was anyone helping her, translating all these orders for her? I had not spotted her in any of the queues.

Two women had fainted in the mid-morning water-queue – was anything going to be done for them?

"They are talking about a sickbay on the upper deck," said Imogen. "A doctor will decide who is to go up there, and there will be a doctor on the deck itself." It sounded eminently reasonable. I forwent the one o'clock food-queue and the 2 p.m. paper-queue and searched for the doctor who was to decide. With effort and persistence I found him.

It was my acquaintance from Karlsbad. We were not pleased to meet again. I wanted a certificate which would entitle me to sleep on deck. "Please." The 'please' cost me a lot.

The doctor remained silent and tried to stare me down. I stood my ground. I explained why I thought I might be entitled to stay in the sickbay. Was he going to have me forcibly removed?

"No certificate," he said.

"I would like to avoid a miscarriage."

Again he waved to an orderly.

"Take her up to the sickbay and give her a stretcher." I was dismissed.

I collected lodencape, blanket, typewriter, camera and the pills the *Veuve* Audouy had given me. If I took them at 2 p.m., there was a chance of avoiding a lengthy queue. The lovers might have found more congenial surroundings. Or given up, maybe?

There was a lot of coming and going in the newly-created sickbay, of noise interspersed by the relentless, forceful *Roskas*. Now they had nothing to do with me anymore, I could not understand them, and no one translated for me.

We heard silence, Thomas and I, in the midst of the noise. We were alone, the two of us, on the overcrowded ship.

By late afternoon the sickbay was full, just two narrow gangways left so that people could get in and out. The places near the engine-room roof were favourite spots – they would be warm at night. A different doctor had been put in charge, a long thin man who walked about rubbing his hands together but asking none of his 'patients' any questions – one had the feeling that he did not wish to become involved. Before dark he became very busy carving out a place for himself and his wife, who was going to join him. He seemed proud of that fact.

The night was surprisingly cold. No longer preoccupied with immediate necessities, I was invaded by my thoughts as if they were enemies finding undefended territory. Eddie's agonized face swam up out of the dark again and again, his hands stretched out as if searching for help. His lorries had broken down; his drivers had deserted him; he struggled to reach a ship and did not make it. Feli threw Fiona numberless times from a balcony and jumped after her to escape an unbearable fate. Jean was dead, dead. Tova padded away on silent paws, the little clouds of dust they set up looking like fetlocks, her eyes asking mine what she had done wrong? I held on to Thomas. I pretended that my cape was a house in which we both lived, safe, warm, untouchable. We were not alone, we had each other.

I looked up at the beautiful sky and wondered if there was any hope for us. There always has to be some who go under.

The dawn brought the coastline back, far, far away, small and hazy. It had no longer anything to do with me.

When we came back from the morning-tea queue on the third day, the sickbay had been emptied of stretchers.

"Why?"

"*Roskas*. So that they can sweep out."

"Will they put them back afterwards?"

"Not till evening."

"Speak Czech, we are all Czechs, speak Czech," came other voices.

The battle-cry "Speak Czech", started in the water-queue, became a *leitmotiv*. The queue had been humming with excitement. Two officers had been arrested during the night.

They had signalled the enemy with a torch!

"Nonsense," said one woman stoutly. "One officer had lost his cap and tried to find it. The other lent him his torch."

"They have put them in chains. They have signalled to the enemy. There will be an air-attack on us any minute now."

"Speak Czech, speak Czech," hissed the queue.

We stood or squatted. The morning seemed endless. Orders boomed out of the loudspeaker and passed me by. The doctor was busy settling his wife in; she was fat, middle-aged and full of complaints.

As if to make up for the lack of food, drink and comfort of any kind, rumours abounded; there was always one woman who knew it all, and what she knew was bad. The woman in the seventh month of pregnancy, already unwell in Agde, was dying. The mother of a small girl was suffering a nervous breakdown and had to be constrained. We were going to be landed in Oran and kept there, while our husbands went to Canada for re-training. We were going to South America, to get us out of the way.

"Hadn't you better go and queue for your midday ration?" An officer had stepped over the ropes dividing the officers' deck from sickbay and tapped me on the shoulder. He was Eddie's age and had spoken in German, seeming unconcerned about the raised eyebrows all around. I explained that I did not think the amount of food obtained was worth the long wait in the queue.

"Would you like a sandwich?" He had one to spare.

"Speak Czech, speak Czech, you are betraying your country," he was immediately attacked by his fellow-officers.

"I fought for the independence of my country when you were still in nappies," my benefactor said quietly. "It isn't by refusing to speak German that we will win." His was a lonely voice.

Later in the evening they put the stretchers back. I wondered if tonight they would bring the pregnant woman up, but they did not. The doctor in charge walked once up and down between the stretchers, rubbing his hands and smiling inanely; otherwise he was busy with his fat complaining wife.

Next morning they told us that in a few hours' time we would reach the port of Gibraltar. If we wanted to change

French money, we should hand it to our officer in charge. The officer who had given me his sandwich came over and translated for me.

"Change our money into what?"

"They did not say."

"Don't talk to him, don't talk to him," a woman next to me whispered. "He is a spy."

A British destroyer had passed us by on the way to the port, and it was leaving port as we came in. No one commented on it. The excitement on reaching Gibraltar was overwhelming, once again temporarily uniting us in hope. Food and water would come aboard. Ships carrying Czech troops had already arrived; others were behind us; we would all be joined together. The rumours seemed to be carried on the wind like seeds, take root and grow with tremendous speed. We dropped anchor in the middle of the harbour.

"*Roskas!* To leave the ship for a swim is strictly forbidden."

"*Roskas!* Queue up for midday rations."

Few of us queued. This was the end of standing in line over an hour for half a spoon of soup or rice, half a mug of water, wasn't it? In a few hours it would all be over. Maybe we would be allowed on shore for a few days, to stay in one of the hotels till further evacuation was possible?

A small boat chuffed towards us, drawing a straight line across the shimmering water. It stopped alongside. A stretcher-case was being brought out – the seven-month pregnancy. An officer was with her, her husband. The little boat set off.

The day wore on. Nothing further happened. We had missed the morning water-queue. We had missed the midday ration. It became exceedingly hot – we had not felt the heat so much while we had been travelling. Now we were standing still, unprotected, in the burning sun of Gibraltar at the end of June.

It seemed long till that day died down. There was still a little hope left at the end of it, the hope of tomorrow. Perhaps it was all going to happen tomorrow?

The little hope made the soldiers on starboard deck sing. It brought the officer 'in charge of supplies', and two of his comrades, up to the officers' deck to strum a guitar. We stood

or squatted and listened. The women on the main deck
ignored the curfew and remained outside to hear better. Only
the women with children had gone to bed.

Light went on in the harbour, light after light. It was
frightening – frightening that there were still lights and
beauty, as if nothing had happened. It broke through your
defences, made you vulnerable once more. A feast under a
starry sky?

No feast, we knew that well!

At nine o'clock came the order to stop all singing and go to
sleep. The stretchers were put up once more. The women
disappeared from the main deck.

The sky did not listen to the order. It remained light for
quite a while longer. The night was warm, and there was hope
for the next day.

We stood for five days and four nights in Gibraltar. No food or
water came on board; none was available. The port was
overcrowded.

The heat was pulverizing. Canvas was put over part of the
small upper deck, but under the canvas the wooden floor
boiled, and outside it the sun and its reflection on the shiny
water blinded you.

One after the other we went down with heatstroke. No one
cared. I tried to exchange my typewriter, my camera, both, for
a pair of sun-glasses. There were no takers. The sickbay
became crowded. Many of us slept on the floor between
stretchers.

Morale deteriorated. The weakest went to the wall.
Stretchers in the sickbay were taken up by officers with 'a
strained wrist' or 'a strained ankle'. The doctor from Karlsbad
occupied a stretcher while his patients slept on the floor,
stepped on by others moving about. The doctor in charge of
the sickbay, the thin fussy, hand-rubbing man, sobbed during
one night because somebody had upset his tin of prunes. He
crawled about in the dark trying to find them by touch on the
filthy floor. "My wife likes them; my wife does like them."

Food and water were given out in ever-decreasing
quantities. It meant queuing up in the merciless sun.

The harbour lights still lit up at dusk. We did not notice them any more.

I held on to Thomas. I hoped that Thomas would hold on to me, that we would both survive. I often thought it doubtful.

Suddenly it was over. Five days and four nights, not even a week. It seemed long at the time.

"*Roskas!* Collect your cases and get ready to leave the ship. Stretcher-cases will be taken off first. Women with children are to go next, the rest to follow in alphabetical order."

The battle-cry of 'Speak Czech, we are all Czech," died a death as sudden as its birth. Everyone spoke to everyone else in any language that would make the other person understand.

"Where do you think they are taking us? Will we find our husbands?" What do you think, what do you think, what do you think?

It did not matter what one thought. It had no bearing on anything. One did not know, only tried to reassure one's neighbour. We were babbling in a mixture of relief, new anxiety, excitement.

The little boat that was to take us around the harbour held about a hundred of us.

"Get a wash, you need one," one crew-member of the *Northmoor* said, smiling, as he helped me into the boat.

As we pulled away, I saw the *Northmoor* as I had first seen her in Sète, a smallish cargo-vessel, flying the British flag. Had we really been eighteen or nineteen hundred people on board? I remembered the "Welcome aboard", the pride with which the sun-burned young officer had put his cabin at our disposal. I thought of the last gesture of the crew, offering to post letters for us from Gibraltar. No, they did not want money for stamps, they would pay for them themselves. The spirit of Dunkirk had been alive in the English crew. Not in us.

I wept.

Had all spirit died in us, the refugees on board? Hunger, discomfort, worst of all the thirst, would leave no permanent scar. The heat had been grim; heat or sunstroke would take a while to get over. Uncertainty about our fate had bitten deeply. But what had turned the journey from Sète to Gibraltar and the time in the harbour into a nightmare was the lack of comradeship among us.

We had all been in the same boat and had disowned one another.

13

Our trip across the port of Gibraltar showed us a splendid sight. We had not realized how big the harbour was. We had not realized that we would be presented with a scene of such beauty.

Once again we tensely studied uniforms from a distance, recognizing Czech troops. The women shouted: "*Nasdar*" across the water, and "*Nasdar*" floated back to us. I had forgotten that there were Czechs other than us. All was not lost.

Impossible to recognize faces: the flash of hope disappeared. Where were they taking us? We busily chuffed towards a ship which looked like a floating prison. All chatter died. Bars in front of the windows – was that the one? Would prison be the next step in our lives? We passed the prison-ship, but the terror lingered. We were moving towards a passenger steamer, called the *Neuralia*, and stopped.

"Disembark in alphabetical order." Up a wooden ladder. We could not climb it fast enough.

Calm, efficient naval officers led us from deck. They showed no surprise at the sight of us; not a facial muscle moved – had they been warned about their cargo? We had come off a coal-ship which had had no water aboard, and every inch of us bore witness to that fact.

We were led to large public rooms.

"Please sit down and wait here until you are called by name."

The rooms were shaded against the sun. Electric fans made a whirring noise. There were easy chairs and settees.

It seemed to me that if it would all end there and then, it would be enough. Shade, the soothing beauty of dimmed light, was overwhelming; the relief of a chair, its arms stretched out, willing to receive me, hold me, support me, indescribable. Not standing in blistering sun. Not squatting with aching muscles. A chair! Sit down and let go, give in.

I thought: "We have come a long way, Thomas and I, and we are still together." It seemed a miracle.

Someone was shaking my shoulder. A voice said urgently: "Come on. Wake up, for God's sake. There is a bed for you in my cabin. They'll put someone else in if you don't come now."

Hedi! I was not even astonished to see her so suddenly. I had not heard my name being called. Three hours had passed. I had seen women get up and leave the lounge, but it had not registered on me. Now the place was empty. Hedi pulled me out of my chair and led me away.

"They called your name three times," she said. "I told Olga to hold the bed, I would go and find you – I saw you come aboard. Hurry."

"What happened to you on the *Northmoor*?" Hedi smiled. "I was all right. I speak a little English now." No wonder she looked less dirty than the rest of us.

The cabin had three bunks. There were sheets and pillows with pillow-cases. There was a washbasin and towels. An Indian steward brought us soap. He was tall and dark; he smiled. He went out, came back, brought us cigarettes and smiled more. His turban made him look even taller. He had beautiful eyes, darker and softer even than Eliane's. His teeth were as white as his uniform. He seemed pleased that we were so happy with his soap, his cigarettes.

There was water in the tap. You turned it on, and water did run out of it. Precious, wonderful water. We tried to make do with the smallest amount, afraid that the wonder might cease. It did not. There was more.

A gong sounded. The steward put his head around the door and said, "Tea is served." He led us to the dining-room. A large room, long tables with white tablecloths, china, cutlery. It seemed a pity to spoil the beauty of it all with our presence, we were so dirty, so unkempt. "Come on, come on," Hedi was impatient again. There was a plate with biscuits at each setting, and Indian waiters brought tea, buttered bread and jam, more tea and more tea. They poured it out of magic teapots which never emptied.

The disbelieving hush of the first few minutes changed into roars of excitement. This was real, and for us, all for us. You ate too fast; you drank too much; you tried to drink for today, tomorrow and the day after. To sit at a well-laid table made it a wondrous feast.

A naval officer held up his hand for silence.

"Will you please keep the places you have chosen for all meals. Dinner will be served at seven. Till then you are free to do as you like."

On our way back to the cabin we discovered bathrooms and showers. There was no holding back any more. If we were to be without water tomorrow, we could cope with that tomorrow; today we would be clean.

Later we went on deck. The little boat that had brought us to our ship was still busily chuffing across the port, carrying soldiers to different ships.

"They all got away," one of them shouted. "Everybody who wanted to, got out. A destroyer stood by and picked up the stragglers. Some of our men went to Bordeaux from the north and were picked up there."

"Are you sure he said 'destroyer'?" I asked the woman who translated for me. I felt excited. I had seen the destroyer. Picking up stragglers?

Hedi, otherwise well-informed, did not know where our beautiful ship was taking us. We asked a member of the crew. He said he did not know; he seemed depressed. They had been away from England for seven months, and for the last four of them they had had no news from home.

The Indian cabin steward was positive.

"England," he said and smiled his bright white smile. England – it would take a fortnight, travelling in convoy. "We'll sail due west first, turn north at the last minute." England? Such a small island, I thought; they would not want foreign women and children there. Canada perhaps? Or America?

On the way to dinner I came upon Renée and her two children in a passageway. The children looked grim. White, thin, covered in eczema. Renée was hollow-eyed, still with that expression of quiet determination on her face.

"Was it very bad?" I asked her.

"It seems better now."

After dinner we were asked to assemble in one of the public rooms for lifeboat drill. At dusk the ship started moving.

Beautiful to see the water streaming by. What destination we were travelling towards no longer mattered. Towards more sorrow? Possibly. Tomorrow! Tonight it was heaven because the ship was moving.

We were steaming out into the open sea. On all sides of us shadows grew out of the dusk. The convoy. A whole world assembled around us, a world of dark, silent shapes. They looked as immovable as mountains. They – and we – stood still. Between us the sea was pouring itself away.

Later, in our cabin, we turned the light on and removed the black-out from our port-hole. If I leaned down from my upper bunk, I could see one of the ships, a dark, reassuring shape, silhouetted against the lighter night-sky. I fell in love with that ship. I loved it that first night and all through the voyage. It was my friend.

The steady noise of our ship's engines, the breathing of my two comrades, was background music which softened the silence. I did not sleep. I did not want to sleep. I did not want to miss any part of that night.

It held the knowledge that Thomas and I were still together. We had come a long way, such a very long way. I had made many demands on a child who stood at the very beginning of its existence. Too many demands. I had needed his help too often. Now I wanted him to rest, to sleep, to be warm and secure in my love. I would try not to touch him with my thoughts. My knowledge of him would be enough.

That night held also the hope of the destroyer, the one which had picked up the stragglers in Sète, overtaken us on our way to Gibraltar and left the port as we came in. Pre-occupied, struggling, blind to so many things, I had noticed that ship both times. Did that mean that Eddie was on it?

I could feel the tension ease out of my body. I had fended off all thought the last few days, alternating between exhaustion and the will to survive. Now the incessant vigilance crumbled, made room for hope: We might still be whole and still be one, Thomas and I, when we saw Eddie again.

It was a night of great tenderness.

At dawn I watched that ship, my friend, slowly detach itself from the dark, till it stood clear and detailed against the morning sky. I was wrapped in fatigue as if in a shroud. I remained in that shroud for the length of the journey.

14

Breakfast next morning was noisily joyful. Still at table, we saw one of the *Gauleiters* marching purposefully towards us. I had forgotten about them, for they had not been allowed in the sickbay on the *Northmoor*. The *Gauleiter* launched herself upon Hedi and announced that she would have to leave the cabin immediately after breakfast, and another woman would be put in. "*Roskas!*" The other woman was on Deck 3; she was ill and needed a better cabin. And Hedi? The *Gauleiter* shrugged. Hedi, the shrug indicated, did not officially exist.

Hedi went in search of a colleague of her fiancé for advice.

"Go and see the English Chief Steward," he suggested. "Leave our CO out of it."

The English Chief Steward took some finding. He was an innocuous-looking man, not very tall, straight and slim, rather formal. Blond, with cool blue eyes and neat, quick movements. I explained why we had come, and he listened without interrupting.

"I will come with you," he said, when I had finished. His voice was surprisingly warm and pleasant.

He followed us to the cabin. The woman had already been installed, a woman of about forty, who had come to Agde after the armistice. Our CO stood in the cabin; the *Gauleiter* busied herself with the woman; a lieutenant stood outside.

The CO gave us sharp, short orders which Hedi translated in a whisper. The woman was sick and incontinent: we would have to care for her. She seemed hysterical, screaming, throwing herself about, trying to pull her hair out. Our CO was on the point of turning round and leaving the cabin when the Steward stepped forward.

He had stood quietly taking in the unpleasant scene.

"This woman," he said, "will be removed to the hospital."
He spoke slowly, trying to make sure that he was understood.
"She belongs in the hospital where nurses, trained for the job,
will look after her." He stopped studying the woman and
addressed himself to the CO. "Anything affecting the cabins
will be decided by me and by me alone. I am in charge. Now,"
he turned to Hedi and me, "if you two would like to go on
deck for a while, I will give the necessary orders to have your
compatriot removed and the cabin cleaned up." He turned on
his heels and walked out.

Hedi and I tiptoed away in his wake. This was quiet
authority *par excellence*. It also was the end of the *Gauleiter* reign.

There was one more Czech clarion-call during the trip:
"*Roskas!* All Czech women without children are to help the
crew in kitchen and dining-room and so express their
gratitude to the captain and his crew."

It was immediately followed by an announcement from the
Captain that we were to do no such thing:

"The Captain wishes to express his thanks to the Czech
Commanding Officer for his kind intention, but ..."

Later the Steward came to our cabin to make sure that all
was well again.

"Come and have a drink with me before dinner. Alex
Brinkley," he introduced himself. "Is everything all right
now?"

His cabin looked like a small sitting-room, with a bureau, a
bookshelf, a couple of chairs and the bunk, hidden by
curtains. He was formal but friendly, the well-educated,
pleasant voice giving everything he said additional impact.
No, he did not know where the convoy was going, only the
Captain knew that. It might be England. He had a wife and
two children in England. It was quite true that they had had
no leave for seven months, that they had had no news from
home for the last four. He was not sure that they would get
leave even if we were going to England; they might have to
turn around and set sail again immediately. From the way he
spoke, we had the impression that we were going to England.

"If we do go to England, will we be interned?"

Mr Brinkley became decisive again. Indeed not! Our men
were allies, having promised to carry on the fight.

"You might have to work, England needs workers."

"What happens if, for one reason or another, you can't work – not for any length of time?"

The cool blue eyes looked at me appraisingly, and I could feel myself blushing.

"Once you are accepted on British soil, you have the same rights, privileges and obligations as our women. The best thing for you is to share a room – that makes living cheaper, take up some work and live as normal a life as is possible in wartime. Come and see me again if anything is worrying you. Come any time you like. Would you like to borrow a book?" he asked me, seeing my glance stray to his bookcase. "Oh, that's the gong for dinner. Come tomorrow and choose one."

We were quiet and thoughtful when we left the Chief Steward's cabin. He had spoken about possibilities we had never dared think of in our panic-stricken speculations. A nearly normal life? It sounded too good to be true. How we could make ourselves useful? Munition-factories? Ambulance-driving? If you were not up to much hard physical work, would languages come in handy? We made elaborate plans!

The public rooms at our disposal and the deck were crowded that night. Social life had started up in a big way and was carried on through the days and nights that followed. The noise everywhere was terrific. I went to Mr Brinkley's cabin in the morning to borrow a book, was invited to stay for a while and stayed on. It was quiet in that cabin. You felt removed from everything, from life itself.

I spent many, many hours during that voyage in the Chief Steward's cabin – silent, serene hours. Our lives ran miles apart, the English naval officer, the Continental refugee – we did nothing to bridge the gap. "Who shall be a neighbour unto him ..." He was my 'neighbour'. Impersonal – held in the grip of his inborn shyness and the naval training – and always kind. Full of carefully-thought-out advice if asked, and never preaching. Not a doctor. Not an ordained man of God. A neighbour. Only when he spoke about his country did emotion come through.

Often I was alone in the cabin while the Steward was busy with his various jobs on the decks. If he was in the cabin, he usually worked on an enormous book which looked like an account-book. He would put glasses on and sit poring over figures, still but for the occasional sigh. Light in the cabin was dim, and he had to turn on a lamp to work by. I was grateful for the dimness, for my eyes had not yet recovered.

"Would you like to turn on the radio? Listen to the news? Or to some music? It won't disturb me."

I did not want to turn on the radio, I was grateful for the quiet. I did not want to know the news – I would have to live them soon enough. From music I ran as if it were an enemy.

I was allowed to be. As tired as I felt. Too tired to move out of a chair. Too tired to read a book. Too tired to think. I lived as if under an anaesthetic.

When it came to his country, Alex Brinkley became single-minded and inspired. He had no doubts.

"We are glad about the Armistice, at least we know where we stand. The Dominions will never let us down. They will fight to the last man. Did you hear Churchill's speech, 'We will fight in the streets, we will fight on the beaches, we will never give in'? That's what he said, that's how it is."

He lived in a world where treachery did not exist, where man believed in man, where people helped each other. This world was contained within the United Kingdom. Wherever our convoy might be going, it would go to one of the countries belonging to the United Kingdom. I remembered the young rating in Sète who had said: "We don't treat dogs like that in England." I listened to every word the Chief Steward said, and I believed every word that he said. It would be all right. It would all be all right.

My cabin-mates were pleasant enough. Hedi, an uncomplicated teen-aged girl from a small village in the Sudetenland, lively, pretty, always in the middle of some happily chattering group, triumphantly brought back to the cabin chocolates or cigarettes she had been given and shared them out between us. Her fiancé, she had been told, was aboard a different ship. Olga had come from Belgium. Her husband had been interned, she said. She seemed ambitious and calculating; however worried she might have been about her husband, it did not show.

Swenska I saw frequently. We did not speak to each other any more. I did not return his greeting. He behaved like a ram let loose among a flock of sheep. I tried not to think about Margit. I could still see her standing on the pier. I could still hear her scream.

The days, punctuated by meal-times and alerts, flowed into each other.

When we turned north, and the glare of sun on water abated, I joined Renée on the upper deck. We sat silently side by side, feeling close to each other. Talk between us would have been like letting the enemy in; pain, fear, self-pity, might have gained the upper hand; one had to be quiet about the past; about the future we knew nothing. We watched her children recover at the magical speed with which children are able to do so. Pierre, her two-year-old, joyfully trotted around the deck, dragging his lifebelt behind him as if it were a toy.

Pilots and air-crews were accommodated on deck-chairs on the upper deck – young men with tight, tense faces, abrasive attitudes, Czechs, some French, many Poles, only a few older officers among them. The hard young faces became soft, the still boyish hands stretched out longingly, when young Pierre toddled by, as if everyone of them knew intimately some small child back home.

From the upper deck I watched the convoy, that source of reassurance.

They were always there, the same ships, at the same distance, in the same formation, day and night. Friends! Comrades! I looked at them last thing at night as I climbed into my bunk; I looked out for them first thing in the morning.

The premature baby girl, born in Gibraltar, died and was buried at sea. The mother, still in a wheelchair, smiled an empty smile to our condolences; the father, stiff and pale behind the wheelchair, politely bowed and bowed.

"The best that could happen to it; the best that could happen to it," the women murmured among themselves – whisper, whisper, whisper, nod, nod. How do they always know? How do they dare to pretend to know?

One evening the usual singsong was usurped by one of the women. She was Belgian and married to a Czech; it turned out that she was a concert pianist. She sat down and began playing the classics – Bach, Beethoven.

We ran, Renée and I. We could not afford to listen. The

time for tears had not yet come, not by a long way.

I continued my life on the fringe. I tried to think as little as possible about the baby, to let it rest. It puzzled me that the boy in my dreams had brown eyes, that the eyes I had felt looking at me had been brown. Eddie and I were blue-eyed! Where did the name Thomas come from? I knew no one of that name. And the little warm hand I could sometimes feel in mine? Did it matter? I was always aware of the baby. Like the sky above me or the air around me, he was there at all times.

I was careful with myself – careful going up or down steps, walking on deck or along corridors. I tried to care for my body because it contained the beginnings of a new life. I was not myself. I was a woman carrying a baby.

It was my baby, I wanted it. It was precious because it was a new life, and all life is precious, doubly so when death is close; because it was conceived at a dark moment in time and seemed the embodiment of hope.

And while I was spinning dreams over an ocean more grey with every day that took us north, a woman who had forgotten all hopes and all dreams threw her child overboard and attempted to jump after it. The child was drowned. The woman was prevented from carrying out her plan. She was saved. Saved!

The news about the bombing of Gibraltar had not reached the women on our ship. The news of a ship torpedoed eleven miles behind our convoy did. In no time at all it circulated on board, viciously embroidered. Our troops had been aboard that ship; the survivors were being machine-gunned in the water.

The woman who threw her child overboard went about it cunningly, so we were told. It had happened on the main deck. She had been standing with a group of women. She drew apart, saying she was going to take her little daughter for a walk on deck. She had walked away, as far away as she could go. She had taken the child into her arms, had hugged it, pointed to the horizon as if to show the child something, leaned over the rail and dropped the girl into the water. Then she had climbed up on the rails herself. She had not been quick enough.

When they pulled her off the rails, she was screaming that

her husband had been on the torpedoed ship; she knew it, knew it for sure. He was dead, she screamed; she wanted to die too. By the time the people around had realized what had happened, it had been too late to save the child.

The woman was taken to hospital and put under sedation. I felt guilty about that child's death. The time to save her would have been before she was driven to desperation. We had all failed her.

One morning we saw seagulls. The seagulls signified the end of living under an anaesthetic, the end of respite. I should have been glad. I was not. Once again a day would have to be faced every day. It seemed too much. I was afraid.

I hung all my fears on the hook marked 'Enemy Alien'.

"You don't understand," I kept repeating to the Chief Steward. "I was born in Germany. I spent the first few years of my life there. I grew up in Austria. I am Austrian, not Czech. I married a Czech, that's all. I don't even know where my husband is."

"I should tell them that," Alex said quietly. "I should tell them all that and look them straight in the eyes while you do so. Try to speak calmly and clearly. You are married to a Czech, who is willing to fight on our side. That is good enough."

I watched the seagulls and thought about what Alex had said. I knew well what he meant. It would be easy to take on the habit of the hunted and look away. To look an official straight in the eye might not be too difficult, to speak calmly and clearly more so. I stammer when I am nervous, or gush.

The gulls brought the return of Czech military orders for us women. Daily alerts doubled and tripled, rigidly enforced now as the danger of mine-fields and air-attacks increased.

Alex Brinkley sat hunched over his big book, more tightly contained than ever. He spent less time on deck; when called out, his very steps were sharper, faster, as if they alone were permitted to express his impatience and longing. Then we saw the first British aeroplane, a coastal-patrol plane with the British markings on its wings. As it flew over our heads, we shouted with joy and waved like mad.

I was suddenly terribly glad that we were going to land in England. I hoped that we would be allowed to stay there not 'safe' in some far-away country but right there, in the middle of it. 'Enemy Alien' or not, this was still my fight as much as anyone's. If I could not personally fight it, I wanted at least to belong to those who could and did, and share with them whatever it might entail.

"*Roskas!* We shall be landing at Liverpool docks tomorrow morning. Your suitcases are to be ready at ten a.m. and stacked in a corner of the main lounge. They will be disembarked for you." It was our last "*roskas*". I did not obey it. Eddie's case had become a link, the only link, between Eddie and me, and I held on to it.

We berthed in the morning. The decks were jammed with people. I slipped into the Chief Steward's cabin to say 'Goodbye' to him.

And 'thank you'? That is very inadequate. Whosoever might cross my path, needing help, however strange and different a person, I was going to try to be a neighbour to him, to pass on the gift I had received. I stammered away. We took it in turns to blush.

He cut me short.

"I want to talk to you," he said. "Sit down a minute. Now! I am going to be very rude. Have you got any money on you, English money? No? I thought not. Well, you cannot go ashore in England without any money. We have a vagrancy law. And I want you to get yourself some shoes. Those rope-sandals are no good in England. It rains too much. It is too wet. The baby will catch cold."

We still took it in turns to blush. The rope-sandals never had been much good.

"Keep the rest of the money," Alex went on, "till you find your husband, till he has got his pay or a job, or till you have a job. I don't need it. If you send it back in one year, two years, any time, it will do. Don't send it back before you can afford to do so. Promise!"

He gave me six pounds.

"God bless and goodbye!"

At lunchtime immigration officers came on board.

"Stay at your place at table and fill out the forms which will be handed to you," we were told over lunch. "Be ready for disembarkation at five p.m."

I noticed that two officials were rounding up some dogs we had aboard, to take them into quarantine. I fought my way through to one of them, faint with the sudden hope surging up inside me.

"Has an Alsatian bitch come ashore on a previous transport? Could you tell me, please – a completely black Alsatian, a bitch?" The man stood still, patiently listening, pulling out a well-thumbed little book.

"A dog?" he said, "An Alsatian dog? Called Titan?" He looked hopefully into my face. "No? Sorry, that's the only one." It struck me as extraordinary that he should be so patient, when he had so much to cope with. I had fully expected a rebuke. Had Eddie not arrived? Not yet? Had he not been able to take Tova?

One of the women learned the address of the Czech camp in England where the first contingent of our men had been taken to. I passed the address on to others. I wrote a letter into the void:

"We are fine. How are you?"

Long before five o'clock we started queuing. We stood with our luggage in our hands, waiting to go ashore. English people were taken off the ship. The sick were disembarked. It grew dark. We stood about, sat down on the stairs, on the floor, stood again. We waited till midnight for disembarkation. The children wilted, whined and collapsed. At midnight we got the order to go to bed.

"Be ready tomorrow morning at eight. Breakfast will be served to you at seven."

The morning was cold, silent and grey. We dressed in silence. We went in to breakfast in silence. We silently assembled on deck. All decks were crowded. For the first time we saw the number of people the ship had carried, in addition to those who had been disembarked yesterday.

Yesterday was a long time ago. The journey from Sète to Gibraltar, from Gibraltar to Liverpool – it was all in the distant past. We were standing jam-packed between the past and future on a raft of uncertainty.

Renée was next to me, once again holding on to her bedsack. I had all my goods: typewriter, camera, lodencape, rucksack, suitcase. I had six pounds in English money and a few francs in one jacket-pocket, an address where I might possibly find my husband in the other. Most probably I carried a baby inside me. There was a new country in front of me, and it was now just two years, four months and a few days since Hitler had robbed me of mine. It felt more like two lifetimes.

PART THREE

The New Country

1

It is not easy to reach the new country.

Few of us have done much honour to breakfast. We have started queuing shortly after seven. We stand, a solid mass of women and children, in the misty drizzle of an early Liverpool morning. We are at one end of the main deck. The troops are assembled at the other end.

At ten o'clock a narrow gangway is put across the gap between ship and port. We are now linked to the next phase in our lives. A wide gangway goes up at the far end, and the troops start disembarking in a steady, orderly two-by-two.

At our end the women surge forward in sudden panic. Children and luggage are in danger of being trampled under. I can see Renée a couple of yards away from me, struggling to keep upright and hold on to Pierre, Martin and her bedsack. I have to fight my way through to her, abandoning my case, which Hedi grabs. We are standing squashed together now, one tight knot in the midst of the seething, hysterical, frightening mass. We move towards the gangway inch by inch. I take Pierre and sit him on my hip, turn towards Renée, to protect myself against sharp elbows and unyielding cases or parcels which dig in, and advance sideways.

It is after twelve when I reach the gangway and struggle not to be pushed to the right or left of it. I have one foot on the small bridge when an enormous push sends me flying across, still with Pierre in my arms. The typewriter clatters to the floor – I must hold on to Pierre, I must hold on to Pierre. Arms grab us before we go over the rails – two English officers have come to our rescue. Hedi shouts behind me: "I have your typewriter, it is all right." We have made it, the four of us, Pierre, Hedi, Thomas and I. We are standing at the edge of England.

"*Geht's?*" asks Hedi in German. Pierre has his two little arms tightly around my neck, tense with terror. "*Es geht.*" It is not true, I am worried by a sudden pain, but there is no time for it now, the trial is in front of me. It starts with two writing-desks at the end of a long corridor, one official behind each one:

"Can I have your form, please?"

The form we have filled out the night before: I have it ready, it is in my jacket pocket.

"And that of the child, please." I have forgotten to ask Renée for Pierre's form; panic mounts in me at my failure.

"It is not my child," I stammer. The official looks up.

"What is the name of the child's mother?" he says quietly, unhurriedly, and another official detaches himself from the wall he has been silently leaning against and goes in search of Renée. He returns with Renée in tow, carrying her bedsack. Both Renée and Martin look exhausted. Pierre stretches his arms out towards his mother and starts crying. The official says "Thank you" to me and nods, I can move on. I meet up with Hedi again. At the entrance to the next room we are halted by another official.

"Wait here, please."

There are several writing-desks in the room in front of us, one official behind each one, one chair in front of each. At present all the chairs are occupied. The interview-room.

Details are etching themselves into my brain. Chairs in front of the writing-desks! We will not have to stand to answer questions like servants in front of their master. The voices, impersonal and quiet. The 'please' and 'thank you'. The well-organized proceeding from desk to desk. Whatever the outcome, we are treated as human beings; we are allowed dignity.

I try to see if there is a woman of non-Czech birth in the interview-room and what happens to her. I am obsessed with my 'enemy alien' origin. "Next please." Hedi and I are in. The moment of truth. "Look him straight in the eyes and answer all questions clearly and truthfully." I stare at the man. I have no confidence whatsoever in justice; there is no justice in war, only expediency. How will I come out of the melting-pot this time?

"Sit down, please. Can I have your passport. Thank you. Now – you were born in Germany?"

"Yes."

"When did you leave Germany?"

"I left Germany as a child."

"With your parents?"

"With my mother. She re-married."

"You were brought up in Austria?"

"Yes."

"Have you any relatives still living in Germany?"

"No."

"In Austria?"

"No."

"When did you leave Austria?"

"In October 1937." Up to now the official opposite me has been busily filling out a form. Now, without raising his head, he looks at me.

"Any special reason?" he asks.

"Personal reasons." It is not sufficient, he is still looking at me. "I had a six-month job in Paris and went to live with my married sister for that time."

"Did you return to Austria at any time between October '37 and the outbreak of the war? No? Did you leave France at all during that time? Have you any relatives left in France?"

"I have a sister married to a French officer." (Have? Or had?)

"When did you last hear from your sister? Where was she when you last heard from her?"

Was Feli trying to reach the south when she wired from Clermont Ferrand? For days I have tried to close my mind, shut out the unanswerable questions, the ever-returning nightmares ...

"When did you last hear from your brother-in-law? Where was he when you last heard from him?"

("... and when God asks me what I have done with my life I will tell him I fought in two wars and did a little painting in between ..." Had Jean spoken his own epitaph? I was not warned that I would be questioned about my relatives. I am not armed! My mind reels under the pressure.)

"You are married, aren't you? Can I see your marriage

certificate, please? Thank you. I see that your husband was born in Brno. When did he leave Brno to go to France?"

"After the Munich agreement."

"When did he join the Czech Legion? What is his rank? What was he in civilian life? Has he any relatives left in Czechoslovakia?"

"We don't know." (Where would they have taken them – to Auschwitz? Or Teresienstadt? Or Treblinka?)

"You did not keep in contact?" The official is sitting up. He has for the moment finished his busy writing. He looks at me. It is a very searching look, and his eyes give nothing away.

"My husband left his mother, who was seventy, his elder brother and a seven-year-old child of a first marriage behind, when he left Brno. He could not take them out. He had no established means of livelihood in France. To keep in contact with them would have endangered their lives. We do not know if they are alive. The extermination of Jews in Czechoslovakia was very thorough."

We are being interrupted. It is just as well. I am carried away on a wave of hate.

"I have a girl here," says the official next to mine, "who is unmarried and has lived all her life in the Sudetenland. What shall I do with her?"

If Hedi had been keen on the 'reunion' of her country with the Reich, she would not have fled. She had no other reasons. I must try to get hold of myself. Not the man's fault that he has to ask these questions, that relatives have become a handle for blackmail.

"Nothing," says the man opposite me. "I have one here, born in Germany, lived all her life in Austria. They are Czechs now, war-refugees." He is not looking at his colleague any more, nor at me, he is writing again.

The dice have fallen. For me they have fallen well this time. I prefer my new designation. I am no longer an 'enemy alien'.

I am being given the chance of a new life. It is something to be grateful for. But I am not unscathed. To be stripped of those you love and the country you love, tossed about in a melting-pot, condemned or redeemed according to the whim of fate eats into you as rust eats into metal. I am kin to every refugee there ever was and those to come. So be it.

"Thank you. You can move on. Next please." I look around for Hedi. She looks pale. I want to speak to her.

"She will follow you in due course," says the official who has interviewed me. It is a definite dismissal. I can see that another woman has already been released from the door. I gather up my belongings.

In the next room I am stopped by a young man standing behind a sort of pulpit, a big book in front of him.

"Have you been in England before?" The book of criminal records – have I a criminal record? The young man goes through the book at tremendous speed. "Thank you," he says and nods towards the next room.

Two long tables at right angles to each other, and a row of people behind them. A young woman waves me to her.

"Have you any personal papers? Letters, manuscripts, drawings, or photos?" I have some letters from Feli in my rucksack. It is all I have left of my sister, I do not want them taken away. "They are in German." I know that there is hostility in my voice. I am prepared to fight for the letters of my sister.

The young woman in front of me looks up. It is not a searching glance. It is a compassionate look from one woman to another. She has brown eyes with green specks in them.

"I am sorry," she says. She means it. "We do have to look at all private papers. Just in case they happen to contain any military information, you know. If they don't, you'll have them back at once. I do read German." She is looking away now. She has noticed the tears which I am fighting down and does not want to witness them.

"Only your luggage now," says the woman, smiling at me and handing me back my precious letters. I stand dumbfounded. I repeat after her in disbelief: "Only my luggage now?" like a child repeating a phrase after the teacher. Have they finished with my papers? Less than an hour has passed since I stumbled into England! I look at the young woman, and she nods, still smiling.

Hedi is still not behind me, nor is Renée. A porter comes up to me: would I like him to carry my luggage? A porter! What a relief. It seems to me that I have heaved my goods around for centuries.

The porter takes my case and my typewriter and marches me to a Customs officer in a big hall.

"Do you have a camera?" the Customs officer asks. He can well see it, it is hanging from my neck. "You will get it back," says the officer. He is bored. "Have you an address in England where we can send it to?" He is talking nonsense: refugees do not get their belongings back, I know that from Paris. I give him my camera. Maybe it is a small price to pay for being allowed to land in England.

The Customs officer hands me a form. He has filled out details of my Rolleiflex, my name, date of landing, name of port.

"Send us this form when you do have a permanent address in England, and we will return the camera to you." He sounds serious. He is examining my typewriter now and my rucksack; then he opens the case, Eddie's case. He goes through it very quickly. There is not all that much in it. He shakes his head, closes the case again, marks it with chalk.

Eddie's case, which seemed so heavy at times, which I arduously lugged all the way from Sète because it meant Eddie to me, was a link. It contains his much beloved winter coat and a hotch-potch of underwear. Triumphant on top of that sits a large breadboard of solid wood, a single white damask napkin, which I have never seen before, and a brown enamelled coffeepot without a lid.

One day, if fate is kind, I shall put that white damask table-napkin of unknown origin on a table and place a bowl with flowers on it. The breadboard will be there and a loaf. The best coffee I have ever brewed will fill the brown jug without a lid. It will all be waiting for Eddie.

And so will I.

And, maybe, Thomas. I realize suddenly that for nearly one hour now I have totally forgotten about Thomas. And that I am still in a lot of pain.

I want to find Hedi, but the porter walks on. "I'll take you to the waiting-room," he says.

The waiting-room is a huge hall. The porter puts my luggage down at the entrance.

"I'll leave it here. You have to go through a health check

first. Over there." Over there is a small temporary building, a nurse receives me, says:

"Wait here, please. All the cabins are full." Another questionnaire must be answered. What illnesses have I had in my life? TB? Any TB in my family? Epilepsy? Anything else I would like to mention?

"I think I am with child."

"How long?" the doctor wants to know.

"The third month probably." He is writing out a label. 'Maternity' is printed in large letters on the label, to which he adds my name, age, sex.

"This label," he says to me, "has to be visible at all times. Fasten it on to your coat or jacket. Here's a pin." I leave the cabin, the label fluttering gaily in the breeze. I am furious, embarrassed by this conspicuous label, by being labelled at all.

There are about eighty women in the vast waiting-room, sitting tidily in order of arrival, on wooden chairs, their backs to the wall. I look along the line of faces, and there is not one I know. Where is soft-eyed Eliane, my companion of the first forty-eight hours? Imogen? The colonel's wife? Renée does not seem to be through either. Surely there is nothing wrong with her papers? A mother, holding on to a little boy of about three, has a big grubby handkerchief in front of her face and is sobbing into it, while the child looks at her. He has a worried, wizened little face and old eyes. Perhaps she will stop crying if someone sits next to her? She lets go of the child, and he scampers away.

I wait. After a while I ask:

"Is there anything I can do? What is it? Have you had bad news about your husband?" She shakes her head.

"It's the boy," she says, wiping tears from red swollen eyes. She speaks German with difficulties. "Everybody ... makes fun ... of him ... because he is so ugly."

Does she know why she is crying? The child is ugly. He is not obliged to be pretty, it is quite immaterial. He is alive! The Gestapo did not get him, nor did bombs, submarines, torpedoes.

"He is fine," I tell my neighbour. "They all go through

awkward phases. He is fine." She looks up wonderingly.

"Do you think so?" she says in her heavy Czech accent. She has spotted my label and now she smiles at me, a childish smile in the tear-stained face. "You going to be a Mamma?" She seems very approving, the childish smile like a present. I am temporarily grateful to my label. Then she calls her little boy, smiles at him, takes him into her arms and hugs him. Now he smiles too, the wizened little face relaxes. He is alive. He is well. He is beautiful!

Tea and sandwiches are being distributed with quiet efficiency by well-groomed women from the WVS. We say: "Thank you, thank you," in whispers. All conversation among us has stopped. I look at the women who, out of their own free will, are distributing food and drink among us. They look pleased with their selflessness. I try to catch the eyes of one of them. They do not look at us, their sisters in the eyes of God. In the eyes of God only? They look past us. Shyness? They do look at the children. Their attitude to the children is friendly, without inhibitions.

Steadily more and more women filter in, occupy empty chairs and are served tea and sandwiches. It is an impressive performance. I can feel someone looking at me. Hedi. She is standing behind an iron gate. She is with a group of perhaps twenty women locked into a small room next to our hall. They look pale and frightened.

"I don't know what is wrong with us," Hedi says. "There seems to be something not right with our papers. We are going to London, same as you, but on a different train. Please write to Michael, tell him what has happened, tell him ..." We are interrupted by an official who says we are not allowed to talk to each other. I nod to Hedi. Yes, of course I will write to her fiancé, Michael. On my way back to my chair I notice that Renée has come into the main hall; Pierre is asleep in her arms, Martin sleeps leaning against her. Renée looks very tired, and the tense determined look is back on her face.

At five o'clock we are told to put all our cases together and board the buses waiting for us.

"No need to rush, you have been counted, there is plenty of room for everyone."

I am still in pain, but I enjoy the bus-ride through Liverpool

– people, traffic, shop-windows, hustle and bustle, life! We are unloaded at a station, told to board a train, two by two – "Plenty of room, don't worry about your luggage, it will be brought along presently." The process is well-organized, handled with great calm. Ours is just one of many ships bringing in war-refugees. They are all coming in at the same time – the moment when Churchill finds it necessary to tell the British Nation: "We await undismayed the impending assault ..." and is talking about the invasion of England – not the influx of war-refugees, although he might well have done so. We are not aware of the possibility of an invasion. We are not aware of the bombing of docks and Channel shipping. The eyes, faces, gestures, attitudes of the British people around us give nothing away.

The train is luxurious. Plush-covered seats, white doilies behind our heads – on the Continent you have wooden seats in the third class!

The compartments are left open, but the carriages are locked once they have their full consignment of travellers. Very young soldiers take up guard-duties in the gangways. We are not going to escape, where would we escape to?

"Where are we going to?" we ask the young soldiers. "To London." So it is London after all.

It is a lovely train journey. Suspended once again, another interval during which fate stands still. Your eyes can feast on a summer countryside, fields with cattle, with hay, busy toy-tractors; and city suburbs with their shabby houses built along the railway embankments – houses which had filled me with horror when I had seen them as a girl. I look at them longingly. They have little gardens. The houses are exactly the same, the gardens are different. Some have a washing-line. The most intimate garments flutter gaily from a washing-line in a country where it is 'not done' to make any personal remark. I have not desired one of the houses before, but I do now. Four walls, a door you can close. Your house. Your door. Your right?

And a cot in one of the rooms? A cooker? A double bed?

At about half past ten we draw into London. We wait in the train till all other passengers have left, then we are shunted to a different platform. Police abound.

At last doors are unlocked, and we walk in twos under heavy police guard to buses. "You'll be taken to the Empress Hall." Where and what is the Empress Hall? How long will we have to stay there?

Two WVS women enter the bus, offer tea and biscuits. I have a biscuit in my hand when a Czech officer opposite me suddenly leans forward. He has come to meet his wife off the train.

"Aren't you Deichslerova?" he asks in heavy German. It takes me a moment to recognize the Czech form of my name.

"Yes, I am."

"Your husband," the officer continues, and immediately I have trouble hearing him through the noise in my ears, "Your husband is in camp. He asked me to tell you, if I see you, that he is all right. He has written to you, care of the Czech Club. He hopes to see you soon."

"Your husband, Mrs Deichsler, he is in England," he repeats.

I nod to show that I have understood. It is the best I can do. I must escape before my face breaks up in front of all these people. I dash out of the bus on legs which threaten to give way beneath me, and a policeman catches me in an iron grip. Does he think I am trying to escape into the undergrowth of Euston Station?

The policeman has me in his arms. He holds me, gently now, against his chest. With his free hand he pats my back. "There, there," says the policeman soothingly. "There, there, there."

I sob my heart out against his shoulder, and the whole bus patiently waits.

2

Arrangements at the Empress Hall seemed fiendish to us. We were unaware of the threat of invasion and of the large number of refugee transports; once through Liverpool we believed ourselves to have been accepted.

Our buses were halted outside the iron gates of the Hall; everyone not part of our transport was required to dismount; the buses rolled into the inner courtyards, and gates clanked shut behind us. We were sorted into two groups, women pregnant seven months or more and mothers with children six years or under to the left, all others to the right. The 'others' were led to a circular arena of considerable size, halved by a heavy tarpaulin. Hefty canteen tables and wooden chairs filled the stage.

"Please sit down. We will bring you tea and sandwiches."

It was about one o'clock in the morning. Later announcements asked us to keep our place at the table at breakfast.

"All tables are numbered. Breakfast will be served to you at six."

I found it difficult to follow the simplest order. The news that Eddie was safe and in England, blocked all understanding. I existed in a bubble of excitement which made everything around me seem unreal.

"Stretchers have been put up for you between the rows. Will you now please go and lie down. Blankets can be drawn at the following points." I forwent the blanket – too much effort. The hall was brightly lit: I tried to find a stretcher in a dark corner, but the semi-circular shape did not allow dark corners. As if to mock my efforts, searchlights were switched on, swept across the rows, stabbed eyes and brain with sharp, pointed fingers. I waited in desperation for those merciless lights to be switched off again, but they were kept on all night. Between short moments of relief one waited for the next penetrating onslaught.

I tried to make a house for Thomas and myself out of my lodencape, tell him that he had a father, hold on to the news that Eddie was in England. The searchlight made short work of the cape and my thoughts. When I left the stretcher to find a toilet, I discovered that there were sentries posted in the gangways.

We were asked to remain at the tables after breakfast.

"There will be a medical examination at ten. You can write letters now if you wish. Members of the committee will arrive at eight o'clock to look after you."

I did not catch the name of the committee. The members arrived, bright-eyed and eager, asked questions, did not listen to the answers, made conversation and did not listen to that either. Obviously their job was to keep us occupied, a thankless task.

For the medical examination a large room had been sub-divided into well-screened cubicles. Six or seven doctors were at work, busily friendly, convinced that we understood no English, amazed at our good health.

"Imagine what they've been through, and look at them. You'd think they'd been on a cruise not on an overcrowded coalship." They did not seem aware that we had changed ships in Gibraltar. Their voices and hands were gentle.

The short examination aimed to spot those who needed immediate attention.

"You're in pain? You'd better see the doctor in the sickroom."

I was given a note. I found Renée waiting for me in the sickroom, shaken out of her self-control by anxiety about me.

"You should have told them when we arrived that you were in pain. I waited all night for you. The label? The label says nothing about pain."

A nurse told me to undress and lie down.

"The doctor will see you in a minute."

The doctor was young.

"Something not right with her," he said to the nurse. "I

haven't time now to find out what. I'll see her again in the afternoon. She can go down to lunch, but she had better stay in bed here otherwise."

I would gladly have forgone the lunch. It was pleasant to lie in bed and think about Eddie. I refused to worry about Thomas. It would all be all right.

At twelve-thirty I was sent to lunch. Two large writing-desks were standing in the hall, when I walked through, a small cluster of women in front of each. Officials were seated behind the desks, high-ranking Czech officers, others who looked like high-ranking English civilians – Foreign Office or Scotland Yard? I stood studying them, puzzled, when one of the women detached herself from the others and came towards me, both hands outstretched.

"Don't I know you?" she asked in an astonished voice. "From Vienna? Of course! I thought I recognized you. Your father's factories were in Czechoslovakia. You must come with us this afternoon. I'll get you through the controls now. Steffi will be so pleased to know that you have arrived in England."

I said: "Thank you very much ..." and tried to conjure up my brightest social smile. I hardly knew Steffi, an unhappy divorcée who had run a fashion boutique in Vienna. The woman who had accosted me I did not remember at all. My stepfather had died years ago.

I accepted undeserved privilege without question or remorse. Anything to get out of the Empress Hall. Might it be the end of being part of mass organization?

Each of the six officials behind the writing-desks went through every one of my papers. They were well-mannered, relaxed and thorough.

"Do you have private means?" one of the elegant Englishmen finally asked me. He misread the astonished look on my face, leaned forward and said in a nearly apologetic tone of voice: "We must make sure. All the women who have passed before you have their own means. They are independent and do not have to be catered for by the Czech Red Cross."

I said: "Of course!" (Look them straight in the eye and speak calmly and clearly.)

"OK. Fine," said the official. He did not ask me what my

means consisted of. "We will call you after lunch."

I went straight back to the sickroom. I was sweating with exhaustion. I told Renée about the latest developments, lay down on the bed and passed out.

I nearly missed my privileged departure! Renée was trying to shake me awake.

"They are calling you," she said. "The women you are supposed to be leaving with are calling you. You must go." She hung my belongings on me as if I were a clothes-horse, gave me a push towards the door. "Don't forget to go and see a doctor soon. *Que Dieu soit avec vous.*"

I tumbled downstairs. Four women were just entering a taxi, among them the one who had recognized me.

"Ah, there you are. I'd better give you Steffi's telephone number. You must ring her. I will tell her that I have seen you."

There were seven of us left. We were joined by a Red Cross nurse. We split up into two taxis, the Red Cross nurse sitting opposite me. She had a worn face, full of little lines, a kind face and a voice that was gentle and matter-of-fact.

"You'll all be tired, I expect. Never mind, you'll soon be in your rooms."

We drove for a long time. London seemed crowded. I recognized the Edgware Road. We stopped nearby. People were walking up and down in front of the house at which we had stopped; they looked as if they were strolling in a village street.

The nurse discovered me when we got out.

"I thought you were six," she said, taken aback. She disappeared up the road.

"Yes," she said on her return. "Three double rooms. Which of you are going to share the double rooms?" Six women left. "I will find a room for you presently. Do you want to share or a room to yourself? Go inside and have a coffee. I'll try to arrange things for you." She pointed to the house, and I went in.

Inside a notice on one door said: 'Czech Club'. Tables, chairs, a waiter: "Can I get you anything?" I sat down. Several men came to my table.

"How are you? Has it been a terrible journey? How many

of you have been released? Are the others all right?" The men spoke in Czech, in German, in English. One of them paid for my coffee, waved any protests aside; another brought a second cup, a piece of cake. "You'd better eat something. I'm sure you haven't eaten a lot lately. Is the nurse looking for a room for you?" The nurse came back and asked:

"How much can you pay per week? Do you want a room with full board, or just with breakfast?"

I was bewildered, but the men took over:

"The Czech Red Cross pays a certain amount of money weekly for each of the refugees who have come over recently," they explained. "Do you want this money used for full board? It means living further away from London. Or do you want it used for bed and breakfast and live nearby?"

"But I said that I had means of my own."

"That's fine," the men said and nodded approvingly. "Then you can have a room nearby with breakfast only." The nurse went off again.

"Has your husband arrived in England?" the men asked. "Do you know where he is?"

Eddie's letter! The Czech Club, the young lieutenant had said.

"Is there ... is there a letter for me ... here ... care of the Czech Club?"

Three of my new-found friends trotted off, came back, triumphantly brought the letter, handed it to me and stood around expectantly. I looked at it. There was Eddie's handwriting on the envelope. And an English stamp. Posted in England. That was enough, it was all I wanted to know at the moment. The nurse came back.

"I have found a room for you, you are lucky, such a nice boarding-house, very clean. Come on now."

I said: "Thank you, thank you," to the disappointed faces around me, the precious letter in my jacket-pocket, my hand holding it there securely. The boarding-house was not far away, a couple of blocks up the road.

A small rectangular room on the fifth floor.

"You can have a bath any time. Now, don't forget, you cannot leave London till you get your English identity-card. It will take six weeks at least, the Home Office is very busy just

now. If you want to change address you must let us know, and
you must let the police know. Breakfast is served downstairs,
between eight and nine. I'll come back and see you later."

I leaned against the closed door and looked at the room. It
had a divan-bed, small easy chair, wardrobe, chest of drawers,
wash-basin. The window was at the far end. The room was
real. It did not vanish as I decided to walk into it. I went to the
window.

A quiet street. Just a few people walking about, a couple of
cars parked near the kerb. There were trees, planted along the
pavement. They seemed far down. Rippling green crowns.
Nice to see the trees!

I sat down in the easy chair and took Eddie's letter out of
my pocket. It did not say much.

"I am all right. How are *you*?" The 'you' was underlined.
"At the moment we are not doing anything at camp. We are
living under canvas." I knew Eddie's dislike of sleeping in
tents. "Do write at once." 'Once' underlined again. I had
already written. I would write again. At once!

It did not really matter what the letter said. Eddie had
written it. He was 'all right'.

I went to the bed and looked at it. On the *Northmoor* I had
dreamed with intense longing of having a bed which no one
could whisk away from me, on which I could lie whenever I
wished, for as long as I wished. I smiled at the bed, patted it
lovingly.

I could not catch up with this being alone in a room, having
a room which was 'mine'. Without an order I did not know
what to do any longer.

I decided to have a bath – an old stand-by in moments of
doubt, fatigue, anxiety. I was in bed by seven. My bed – for
the time being. I could hear cars, buses – the Edgware Road
was not far away – occasional footsteps. I could hear birds. It
seemed a long time since I had heard birds other than seagulls
with their raucous noise.

I watched the sky grow dark. I had never before realized
how beautiful, how blessed, darkness can be. I missed my
friend, the ship from the convoy. I thought I would make the
tree in front of the house into a friend.

I travelled all night in my restless sleep. Eddie's letter was under my pillow. I thought it would reach me from there, but it did not. I had not received it, had not arrived in the room, had to rediscover it all when morning came.

The pain was better. The tree was still there – I shot out of bed to look for it.

The dawn chorus had woken me. I watched the birds for a while, busily fluttering about, gay little miracles with two wings, twittering away in the language of heaven. They looked so small and seemed to know how to live their lives.

I envied them that knowledge.

3

During the first few days in London I went from nowhere to nowhere. Down five flights of stairs to the Czech Club, up five flights of stairs to my room, the only exception a short walk to some shops nearby in a street running towards Paddington.

Thrilling to discover shops! I bought writing-paper, envelopes, a pen, stamps, a bar of soap. I discovered a cleaner, handed over my cape.

"Can I have it back soon, please."

"Ten days," said the girl behind the counter.

"But ..." I had reckoned on the cape to hide my inelegant attire.

"There's a war on, don't you know?" The girl seemed proud that there was a war on, happy that it enabled her to be so unpleasant. I fled, desolate at the loss of my cape, the unfriendliness.

The boarding-house shared its facilities with several adjacent houses. One breakfast-room, a sitting-room, a reception-desk and three telephones served them all. We, the newly-arrived Czechs, met at breakfast; more women had joined us after their release from the Empress Hall. We greeted each other joyfully, effusively at these first meetings, gossip and queries bounced from table to table across the room. I sat transfixed by the baleful looks of the English residents. I had been to England before, knew a little of English habits; my companions remained unaware and undismayed. All Continentals are noisy by English standards – we were even noisier than normal, excited, glad to have arrived, to be alive. The louder we became, the more stony became the silence around us.

The battle at the reception-desk was as loud as breakfast

during those first few days. It was difficult for anyone to move through the throng of women debating news from their husbands in camp, impossible for the diffident English who just stood there, chin up, mouth tightening, patience fading from their faces, disapproval in its place. The rush to the telephones was no better!

I entered the sitting-room once on my busy excursion from nowhere to nowhere. I opened the door quietly – and was nailed to the spot by the piercing hostile glances. I felt like the knife-thrower's mate. One wrong move and the next knife would go through me. I retired fast. Were they holding a wake in there?

I felt sorry for the manageress, all prim and starched, polite and unapproachable, her hair too tightly waved, her voice too flat. I need not have been. Prim and starched, she coped. Unfailingly polite, she announced that breakfast would be served to us in a small separate room – "so that you can be among yourselves", post would be brought to us there. The onslaught on the telephones died a natural death.

No further letter had yet come from Eddie. I had received no telephone call. The letter addressed to me care of the Czech Club lost its power.

During those first few days some of the women still came to visit me in my fifth-floor room, bringing news from the Empress Hall. Renée had been released and evacuated to the country. Her husband had been found – he had come via Bordeaux. Splendid news! I was happy for Renée. I wondered what an English landlady in the country would make of the bedsack?

Hedi had not been seen or heard of, and nothing was known of those with her. Several of our women were in a Liverpool hospital, ill with the after-effects of our *Northmoor* journey, not least those caused by the toilet-arrangements. The woman who had thrown her child overboard had been taken to a mental hospital in the south.

"Do you remember Mrs Kreibl? The woman who was so heavily pregnant in Agde already? She's had twins! They took her to hospital in Liverpool as soon as we berthed. Her husband had been informed by radio from the ship.

"She had a little boy the same afternoon, and a baby girl

shortly after, very, very weak. The doctors weren't sure that they would be able to pull her and the baby girl through.

"Kreibl was not allowed to be with his wife. He waited on the hospital steps, the only place to smoke, apparently. All night. A policeman waited all night with him. They could not speak to each other. I suppose you don't really have to speak in moments like that.

"The policeman fetched him a cup of tea in the middle of the night and a sausage roll. He gave him the thumbs-up sign shortly after dawn, shook Kreibl's hand and left. Kreibl was allowed to see his new family later in the morning.

"Can't see any of our policemen behaving like that, can you?" my visitor concluded thoughtfully.

After those first few days, contact ceased; we became strangers. My main refuge during that time was the Czech Club. It offered food at reasonable prices. One cup of coffee would see you through the afternoon. I went there when I longed to be among people; I shot back to my room because the people had nothing to do with me.

The occasional visits to the little shopping street apart, I had the company of the ever-more familiar tree, the birds and the sky over London, a clear sky as yet. It was not such a clear sky over other parts of the country. The Battle of Britain had begun.

At last a letter for me did arrive. It did not say much, did not mention Tova. The Czech officers were still under canvas. Nothing was as yet known about their future. Like the troops they received two shillings pay per day. Eddie would try to get leave as soon as possible.

"Go and see a doctor ... go to the Czech Red Cross, they can put you in touch with a hospital ... look after yourself ... see you soon ..."

I sat a long time over the letter, trying to read what was not written. I thought it time I rang up Steffi. I waited till the telephone rush was over, diffidently went to the telephone-booth and noticed the manageress standing straight and stiff behind the reception desk. She was looking at me with thoughtful eyes. She gave me a fleeting smile. It came and went in a flash.

I had not thought that she could smile, certainly not that

she would smile at any of us. I was pleased with that smile, proud of it, greatly encouraged.

That telephone call nearly failed. I had expected someone to say: "Stephany Bolt speaking", but a deep voice had stated firmly: "Mrs Bernhard here." I asked anxiously: "Steffi?"

"It's you!" said the voice at the other end full of emphasis. "Melanie told me that you'd arrived in London. When can you come over?"

"Any time you like. This afternoon?"

"We are in Arlington House, just past the Ritz, on your right, you can't miss it. Arlington House in Arlington Street, flat six. Around four?"

The Ritz! I had to cross Piccadilly to get to the Ritz. In sandals, slacks and shirt? I had not bought the shoes yet, had not dared to spend money on anything except food, postage, the piece of soap, cigarettes.

"I am ... not very well dressed."

"No ..." said Steffi. It was a long drawn out 'no'. "I don't expect you are. Don't let it worry you. Apartment six, don't forget."

She hugged me when I arrived. She stepped back, looked me up and down, said: "Let me see ... yes, that will be all right ... I thought I could trust my memory ... come with me." She took my hand, dragged me behind her, stopped, looked up into my face, nodded and said: "Hairdresser!" A statement, not a question.

The room she led me to was a bedroom. Carefully laid out on her satin-quilted bedspread was a collection of clothes, from underwear to jacket, the famous 'Stephany' accessories included. She busily picked up a skirt, held it against me and nodded, satisfied. "Yes. It will fit. I thought I'd remember your size. Had a bit of a whip round," she explained.

"Let's go into the other room now and have coffee. You can try those on later. Any small alteration I can do for you. Now come and sit down and tell me all about it."

My mind usually goes blank if anyone asks me to tell them 'all about it'. At that moment, in the elegant flat in Arlington House, the task defeated me altogether.

"I am married," I said flatly. "And I believe that I am pregnant."

Steffi immediately stopped being lively and busy. She looked up, her unhappy restless eyes searchingly focused on my face.

"Do you want to see a doctor?" she asked.

"Yes. Please."

"Uncle Schiff. Are you in a hurry? Yes? All right, I'll ring him now. He is marvellous."

She went out and was away for a long time. I wondered why she was phoning from another room, there was a telephone right here. I felt like a traitor to Eddie and the Czech Red Cross. But no more mass arrangements, wards, queuing, no more 'Orders'.

"He'll fit you in tomorrow morning at eleven. Special favour to me. He is in Wimpole Street, I'll write the address down for you. Don't worry about the bill, I have a running account with him. Old Bernhard won't know any different."

Later I tried the clothes on, and they fitted. I found twenty pounds in a handbag and did not want to take them.

"Twenty pounds," said Steffi disparagingly, lively and bright once again, "How far will twenty pounds get you?"

"Eddie will get paid in due course."

"Army pay! You hold on to the twenty pounds. You'll need them."

I tried to thank Steffi, but she refused all thanks.

"Tell me what Uncle Schiff says ... ring me. Or no, I'll ring him myself. Good old Uncle Schiff, marvellous man. Come to dinner. Not tomorrow, we are out tomorrow, the day after tomorrow, all right? At seven, or before. Let's have some drinks first."

I walked back. I was rich, I could have taken a bus. I wanted to walk.

We were going to see the doctor tomorrow, Thomas and I. I thought: "Thomas, Thomas, Thomas." Every step I took said "Thomas".

I relished having a nightie to go to bed with, put Eddie's letter under my pillow, worried lest I had walked too much, slept my haunted sleep, woke with the birds and did not cease to pray: "Thomas".

I took a taxi to Wimpole Street. By ten o'clock that morning I felt too weak to do anything else.

4

The waiting-room is large, elegant in an old-fashioned way. People sit stiffly on expensive and uncomfortable chairs, frozen into place, ignoring each other politely. Silence, not even the rustling of clothes. Is it too late to run away?

It would not be clever to run away.

Through corridors and up in a tiny lift, guided by the receptionist.

"Mrs Deichsler to see you, doctor."

Two hands warmly enclosed my hand. Eyes peer at me through thick glasses, under bushy brows. I am being helped into a chair. The doctor walks round his writing-desk, sits down opposite me. He has a note-pad in front of him; a yellow pencil lies next to it. He leans over his writing-desk and studies me intently. His eyes look enormous behind these thick glasses. Light from two windows behind him falls disconcertingly bright on my face.

"How long since you arrived in England? Nearly ten days? Had a rough passage, yes? Been in pain lately, yes? Tell me about it."

The doctor has a round face, a round Jewish face. He is very ugly, his hair is as untidy as Eddie's.

"Relax," says Dr Schiff suddenly. "Forget the trimmings, part of the job. If you want to get anywhere as a specialist in London, you have to have rooms in Harley Street, or Wimpole Street. Doesn't mean a thing. Don't let it worry you."

I find my tongue. I say what I have to say. It does not amount to all that much.

"All right. Don't worry. We'll have a look."

Returned from the examination, I re-discover the doctor behind his writing-desk. He is making notes on a card. I wait in that dreadful suspense which precedes a doctor's verdict.

Why does he not say anything? I am looking at him, but he does not look up. He does not write any more either. Guided by his fingers, the yellow pencil is doing somersaults.

"Well, yes," he says hesitantly. He has taken off his thick glasses. Without the lenses his eyes look small and very tired.

"Well, yes," he starts again. He seems to have come to a decision. "I understand from Mrs Bernhard that you are in a – hm – difficult situation, yes? I mean, she said ..." His words trail off. His lower lip seems to lead a life of its own. It is a full lower lip, and he pushes it out, pulls it in again, bites on it.

What is he trying to tell me?

"Am I pregnant or am I not pregnant, Doctor?"

"Oh, you are pregnant all right. About thirteen weeks."

"And ... everything is all right ... normal ... more or less all right?"

He looks up. He puts his glasses back on, the enormous eyes studying me intently once more. The lower lip stops leading a life of its own, and the pencil lies still on the desk.

"D'you want it to be all right? Yes? You are not frightened? You want the child? Don't cry."

I do cry, I cannot stop myself. I cry about that first glorious moment of strength on the *Northmoor*, and the days and nights of horror that followed it. I cry about the unreal hours in Alex Brinkley's cabin and his quiet voice, which tried to lead me back to life. I cry about my fear that I, and the unborn child in me, might be rejected in Liverpool, and the relief at not being rejected. I cry because we have found Eddie again, and he is safe. Most of all I cry because Thomas is real; I had hoped so desperately he would be and had been so afraid. There are oceans of tears in me.

"It's all right." Dr Schiff beams at me. "There are complications, not bad ... sufficient if you hadn't ... if you didn't ..." His voice trails off. "You will have to take life quietly. Lots of rest, no carrying of anything heavy."

"What about work!"

"What work?"

"War-work. Aren't we all needed to help in the war-effort?"

"No work! Rest! Now, I want all the details. Where is your husband? When will he get leave? I want to see him. I'd better

have his address. Do you eat all right? What about sleep – do
you sleep all right?"

"The nights are bad."

"Very bad? I'd rather not give you sleeping-pills just now.
I'll give you some iron. Tell me if you can't keep the pills
down. Vitamin injections, twice a week to start with. The pain
should wear off, but you must tell me at once if it gets worse.
At once, d'you hear!"

Vitamin injections twice a week? In Wimpole Street?

"No charge." Dr Schiff shakes his head. "One refugee to
another, yes? Yes! Of course. You don't know when your
husband will come on leave? Well, they'll have to give him
leave some time, won't they? So, see you next Friday. Take it
easy. Don't forget the pills."

The doctor gets up, comes over to me, takes my face
between his two hands and gives me a smacking kiss on each
cheek.

"You're a beautiful girl," he says. "You'll have a beautiful
baby. We'll have a beautiful baby together."

Papa Schiff! How could I ever have thought that he was
ugly?

I walked away on a cloud. Thomas was real. It seemed
almost too much happiness to bear.

In the evening of that day, lying in bed, it dawned on me
that my request to see a doctor in a hurry might have been
misinterpreted by Steffi. Fear of so vast a misunderstanding
sent shivers down my spine. But terrors haunted me every
evening, waiting in shadowy corners, ready to pounce.

I would see about Steffi tomorrow. Thomas was with me;
Eddie was in England and safe. Enough unto the day. I would
see about Steffi tomorrow.

She was busy with preparation for a meal when I arrived. I
sat in the kitchen, a drink in my hand. There was a wall
between us.

"Not all plain sailing, I gather," she said without looking at
me.

"It will be all right."

"Well, you must know what you are doing!"

There had been a misunderstanding.

I met 'Old Bernhard' later on. He seemed a fussy little man, older than his wife. He had come to England from Germany, was now more English than the English. I noticed that immediately on arrival he obsessively straightened out pencils, pictures, ashtrays, which had all seemed straight and in their proper place before.

Other people arrived, for drinks, for dinner, some after dinner. I became a news-item and was handed round with the drinks. One man was interested in the fact that my husband was an engineer, had worked in sawmills and was knowledgeable about laminated wood. He was a naturalized Pole and had a factory in North London which produced propellers for Spitfires. Steffi described him as 'Uncle Nick'. She called all her male friends 'Uncle'.

"Poor old Uncle Nick. His wife ran off with some other bloke at the beginning of the war. He lives in lonely splendour in Mayfair and spends all his free time at the Ritz. Or with us."

Arrangements for other cocktails and dinners were made during the evening, summer holidays discussed. Someone was having a new flat in London re-decorated. Steffi described the house she and Bernhard were buying out of town.

I was sorry that I was not supposed to walk home. Blacked-out London had a mysterious air: buses and cars with shielded lights looking like monsters with sleepy eyes, sliding on silent feet towards unknown destinations.

I felt confused. Where was the war? Cocktails and dinners, holidays, re-decorated flats, new houses? Air-raids and bombs, the threat of invasion, discussed as if it could only happen somewhere else?

What was happening to me? Was our new life going to be based on the help of the Czech Red Cross, some people I had known in Vienna and Eddie's two shillings pocket-money? Was there nothing I could do to earn my living?

Was I irresponsible? Steffi had indicated as much. The thought had never entered my head.

In my room the terrors were waiting in the shadows. I watched the birds enviously. They had a place in the order of things. I had not yet rediscovered mine.

Where was Eddie? When was he going to get leave?

5

Before long some of the shopkeepers in my chosen street detached themselves from the backcloth of their shops, stepped forward and became a sort of second-line family.

The woman at the corner greengrocer's was the first one who spoke to me. She was tall, four-square and grumbly, wore sack-like garments and had a kind of pudding-basin hair-cut.

"And where do you come from?"

I told her. I added that the Merchant Navy had got us out of France.

"My boy is in the Merchant Navy," she said.

"You must be proud of him. Is he all right? Have you heard from him?" She shrugged her shoulders.

"Never hear from him. Kids, they are no good to you. I've had five. Three boys and two girls. I should know."

"Do you live with one of your daughters?"

No, she did not live with any of them. She had a little flat of her own, on the top floor, just around the corner.

"I've got my job, and I've got my flat, and that does me. It's all I need."

She was on the defensive, seemed lonely. I was shaken. I had taken it for granted that elderly parents, especially widowed elderly parents, lived with one of their children. We chatted daily over the sale of two apples.

"Little Old Hitler will get a surprise when he tries to come here. We'll show him what's what."

Next to the greengrocer's was a small radio-shop. A single window displayed its goods, second-hand radios mainly, against red curtains. Sometimes you discovered a pair of dark, intense eyes looking at you just above the curtain-rail.

The second-hand radios seldom changed, but I studied

them often. One day I might be able to listen to music again. Through the glass door I could see the shopkeeper sitting in a cubicle at the back of his shop, bent over valves and wires, a soldering-iron at his side. Several times our eyes met above the curtain-rail; he had decided to get up, stretch his legs. One day he came out of his shop.

"Are you interested in radios? Where do you come from?"

He was a boffin, a backroom boy. He was well informed. We started talking about the war, the raids on Channel shipping, the number of aircraft shot down, the evacuation of children from London and coastal towns. It was a relief to be able to talk about the war.

"Do you think they know what they are talking about when they speak so blithely about the invasion?" I asked him one day. He nodded. It was a disconcerting habit of his to nod at all times.

"No," he nodded, "Not really, I suppose. But they'll die to stop it just the same."

The bakery came next. It was run by a thin spinsterish woman of uncertain age, indignant if you wanted bread, irate if two people wanted to buy bread at the same time. She closed the shop as soon as the daily delivery was exhausted.

The grocer's name was Mr Samuel. He wore khaki-coloured overalls, and one did not remember his face because it was so ordinary; one did remember his gestures and the gold-rimmed glasses he wore. He knew his customers well, closely followed their ups and downs. On a shelf behind the counter, leaning against cans of Heinz Tomato Soup, he kept a photo of a house. Occasionally he would take the photo down, give it an ardent kiss, put it back on the shelf again. The house was somewhere in Palestine; the connection between him and that house I was not able to establish.

One of his daughters occasionally tried to help him in the shop. She was defeated not only by the regular change-around in the stock-room but also by the change-around of moods and instructions.

"No, Father says you can't have any more goods on credit," I heard her say one day to a scruffy lad of about ten. "Father says ..."

"Give him the goods," interrupted Mr Samuel.

"But, Father, you said ..."

"I said, I said, I know what I said! You want I should send a child away hungry? God forbid."

There was a watchmaker, a sub-post-office, the cleaner, a second butcher on the opposite side of the street, but they did not become part of my family. There also was a fishmonger. I did not get to know the fishmonger till later.

I made one more attempt to make contact with former acquaintances, paying a visit to the Selsdon Park Hotel to look them up. I came away in tears. There was no bridge between those touched by the war and those as yet untouched.

Hair-dos and fashion. Golf and bridge.

"When are you leaving for Canada? Next week? We're leaving this weekend for the States."

On the way back in the train a woman asked me if I was all right.

"Yes, thank you."

"Where do you come from?"

"Czechoslovakia."

She ran after me at Victoria Station, caught me up and put a hand on my arm.

"I just wanted to say ... I wanted you to know ..." she stammered. "We did not all agree with Chamberlain ... you know ... with Munich ... we were shocked ... ashamed. I am sorry."

I did not deserve her sympathy, I was not Czech. But she more than made up for the Selsdon Park Hotel.

Papa Schiff shook his head and said he thought I would make better progress.

"Do you eat enough, yes? Do you sleep all right?" Huge behind the thick lenses his eyes were burning holes into my weak lies. Oh yes, I ate well, I slept well.

"Hmmm," said Papa Schiff, "When is your husband coming on leave? It's about time, you've been in England how long now? Four weeks."

We were playing a game of make-believe, I pretending all was well, he to believe me.

"The nights are bad," I admitted.

"Bad in what way? I'll give you a different medicine, try that for a week. Here." He handed me a bottle from his cupboard. He seemed preoccupied, shook his head when I left, let me go without the traditional two kisses.

I had not been doing a lot with myself. I had visited Steffi; they were going to move out of London soon, had twice been to dinner with 'Uncle Nick', whom I called more respectfully 'Mr Serge'. He was a lonely man, keen to have company.

The nights were bad. I became frightened of falling asleep, nightmares held me in such an iron grip. There was only one solution for me in my nightmares – to jump down to the tree so blatantly green and luscious, not a friend, a hostile bystander, whose very branches taunted me. I awoke to find myself standing in front of the window.

I asked Miss King for a room on a lower floor. She gave me one on the first floor, its window looking out on a small garden. I closed the window at night and tied it up with string before going to bed. Awake I could hold on to Eddie and Thomas; in my sleep they were gone.

I, like Papa Schiff, very much wanted to know when Eddie would come on leave. He had applied several times. He would wire if he did get a pass. He was trying to learn English. There were too many officers in the Czech Army contingent which had come to England, he wrote, an officers' battalion was going to be formed.

Letters from Eddie I carried for days in my handbag. None of them so far had mentioned Tova.

I had started to day-dream about having a dog. Any dog ... any small dog. A companion! Something warm and alive to care for. My mind was filled with Thomas. My hands were empty.

My nightmares began to be topped by a different dream. I explained again and again to Eddie why I had had to get myself a dog.

On my next visit Papa Schiff was in a gay mood. "Cheer up, cheer up, it'll be better soon," and two smacking kisses. It made no dent in my longing for a dog.

The papers reported a bomb-attack on Croydon Airport. I wondered about the bridge- and golf-players. The sirens had sounded in London as well. I had heard them with my ears and the pit of my stomach.

No news from Eddie on Friday morning. No weekend pass.

I went to a home for lost dogs. Which of the many should I save? I left empty-handed, owing one dog a chance. There had been too many – how could you choose? I was desolate.

No news from Eddie on Saturday. Another endless, barren weekend in front of me.

I scoured the pet-shops of the neighbourhood. I found a dachshund bitch puppy.

"Last of the litter. Didn't really mean to sell her."

Forty-five shillings, collar and lead thrown in? The puppy was warm and alive in my hands.

Obsessed, I rang the boarding-house at twelve, at one, at two o'clock. "No message," said the girl on the phone. "But ..." I heard her say as I put the receiver down. I dialled again.

"I just wondered," said the girl in the same polite, impersonal voice, "Did you know that your husband is here?"

"My husband?"

"He has been waiting for you for over an hour."

I took a taxi home.

6

Eddie was lying on my bed on his back, his hands under his head. He lay so still I thought he had fallen asleep. Then he slowly rose, stood motionless.

He looked ill. He had lost weight. The eyes were too light a blue. For a moment, as if the wrong side was being projected, I saw his face again as I had last seen it in Sète, heard him say: "Careful of the step. God bless you." That was over now. Finished! But never again like that, hapless and torn asunder.

I closed the door behind me, put the puppy down. I thought: a new country, a new chance, equal obligations and equal rights. Like an old skin I shed the insecurity and confusion of the first weeks in England. I was no longer lost. I did not envy the birds. The tree was just a tree. The three of us had arrived. Whatever came next we would face together, take it from here.

We looked at each other for a long time, Eddie and I, frightened to move, to touch. I was sorry that Eddie looked so ill. It would pass. I was aware that he would have to go away again, soon, within hours – how many hours? It had to be faced, it was part of our new life.

We slowly moved within reach of each other.

"Why didn't you wire?"

"I didn't know you had a dog!"

We spoke simultaneously. I was appalled at the thought that I had not been there when Eddie arrived.

"No time," Eddie said. "The letter was only handed to me last night, after the CO had left. I had to wait for this morning to get a pass. Only just made the train."

"What letter?"

"From your doctor, didn't you know? He wants to see me. What's wrong?"

Papa Schiff? Why?

"Nothing is wrong. Papa Schiff probably thought it was time we saw each other again."

And the dreaded question:

"Who gave you the puppy? Why a dachshund?" Bad conscience made me quite incoherent. "Tell me slowly. Calm down."

I told him slowly.

"What's wrong with your window?" Eddie wanted to know later.

"Nothing is wrong with my window. Why?"

"It's all tied up with string."

"It rattles," I said lamely.

"String won't cure that," said the *Herr Ingenieur* from Brno. I watched him as he painstakingly folded strips of newspapers ponderously stuffing them between window and frame.

"There," he said proudly. "That will cure it – why are you smiling?"

"Because I'm happy."

Over supper at the Czech Club he told me that Tova was alive.

He had left her with one of his men who had chosen to stay behind in France.

"He begged me not to shoot the dog. A very good chap. I do trust him."

My mind immediately started churning out 'ifs' and 'buts'. No use. If she was happy, I was glad that she was alive. 'We', Tova and I, were still dead.

How painfully alive death remains.

He had been on the destroyer, Eddie told me, and had had a lot of trouble with his lorry-drivers. Some he had had to force at gun-point to carry on. He did not want to talk about it. I did not want to talk about my journey either. It was over.

Camp was unpleasant. Since arrival he had shared a tent with three other officers. There was nothing to do but play cards, get rheumatism, learn English.

There was a surplus of about seventy officers over forty, not

fit to join the officers' battalion. Their future was undecided.
They might be released for war-work or be kept 'in reserve'
and given a small pension. Forty seemed young for the
rubbish-heap.

"What about the doctor? *Mon poète?* Toni?"

Eddie shrugged his shoulders. He knew nothing of any of
them.

Michael had joined the officers' battalion.

"And Hedi, what happened to Hedi?"

Hedi had just been released from Holloway Prison. She had
been there for four weeks. He did not know on what charge.

"She and Michael are going to get married. Any day now."

I remembered my suitcase at some point.

"Did you bring it? Do you still have it?"

He still had it. He had forgotten all about it. He would
bring it next time. He was due for his real leave. This was
compassionate leave, a present from Papa Schiff.

On Monday morning we went to see the doctor. I had to
wait in the secretary's room, while the men had a 'serious
talk'. I was to take a one-room flat as soon as my identity-card
arrived, they decided, where I could cook for myself. AND
WOULD DO SO. I would have to take sleeping-pills. No
more fibbing! One hot meal a day at least.

"If the pain increases, you are to phone me at once!"

"Splendid idea, the puppy," said Papa Schiff staring at it
through thick glasses as if he had never seen anything of the
kind before. "Gives you something to do. See you Friday. Next
week we'll start cutting down the injections to one a week."

Eddie looked battered when we left.

"You do realize, don't you, that it might all come to
nothing? I mean, Dr Schiff has tried to tell you, he says you
don't listen."

"It will be all right."

"But there is a risk."

"In addition to the odd bomb or two and the invasion?"

We were walking towards the station.

"What will you do if they really start bombing London? Go
to a shelter?"

"Hide under the bedclothes with Titch."

I could not bear the look on his face. As the train pulled out, I shouted as loud as I could:

"It will be all right, Eddie. I know it will be all right."

Haunted faces blotted out by distance. How long would one have to live with them?

When I dropped in at the boarding-house after Eddie had gone, I found that my identity-card had arrived. It was a mottled blue and described me as: 'YAKA 2326847'. Obviously there were over two million of us, but I never knowingly met another YAKA.

7

The bath was painted in thick blue oil-paint. It stood in the kitchen. Bath and sink were served by an elderly geyser. Cough, cough, splutter, splutter, it did not like new tenants and made no bones about it. The furniture too had seen better days. So had my future landlady and her husband. Grey hair, light eyes – life seemed to have washed most of the blue out of them.

"I am sixty, and he," a thumb pointing at the shadowy figure behind her, "is eighty."

They looked the same age. My landlady wore felt-slippers and had her hair in curlers. During all the time that I was to live in their house, I waited for the supreme moment when her hair would not be in curlers, when it would appear, triumphant, in its desired shape. The moment never came.

The flat was beautiful. It was on the first floor and looked out on to the street. It had a reasonably sized kitchen, with a table and two chairs, a cooker, saucepans, frying-pan, tea-kettle. It had a room as well, but it was the kitchen which made it into a home.

They did not have a shelter. They had turned their bathroom into a sort of shelter, did I mind? Weren't the sirens awful? They were living on the ground floor; the bathroom had sandbags outside, sandbags inside and a board across the bath to sit on.

"You will have to share the toilet with one other tenant on the first floor. The two people who have the large flat on that floor have their own, been with us for years they have. There are three girls sharing the top."

Monotonous voices, hesitant gestures, slow, shuffling steps. They were gentle, and they were afraid.

The flat was half the price of my room in the boarding-house. I informed the police, the Czech Red Cross, Miss King. It was all going to happen. In a week's time.

During that week we had our first all-night alert. One could hear the planes overhead. They passed over and dropped their bombs on Merseyside.

Towards the end of the week Eddie arrived, unannounced and unexpected. He looked worse than before. He had a forty-eight-hour pass.

He was, he said, expendable. No use to the army. A write-off. Would it be best to accept the small pension, live in the country somewhere, grow cabbages? Now that we had bombed Berlin, London was bound to be bombed.

After a while Eddie agreed that a child needed a future and that growing cabbages in the country might not be the right one.

There would be difficulties to be overcome, language for one – we could tackle that between us once Eddie was back. Clothes – would he get a demob suit? We would have to live where war-work of the engineering kind was available, and wherever that was there would be bombs. We might just as well stay in London. In London I knew 'Uncle Nick', and there was Steffi in the background.

We! For the first time since we had met we were not scheduled to be split apart. We would face air-raids together. We would face invasion together. Whatever came next ...

Would the bombs hold off till Eddie was back?

The departure from the boarding-house was unemotional. During all the time there I had not once spoken to any of the residents. What was this tremendous fear of human contact which the English seemed to have? Why could they not carry a smile on their sleeves?

Eddie moved me into my new home and immediately afterwards left. It would be two or three weeks, he reckoned, before he would be back.

"Stay here, don't come to the station with me, I can't bear to see you standing there."

"Two to three weeks, it's nothing," I said brightly. What else was there to say?

I loved the flat. I could have a cup of coffee or tea whenever I wanted, close the door and *be*. Sharing the toilet with one tenant was no hardship; sharing the kitchen with mice was. They were tactful during the day and thought that I should be tactful at night. Beyond my power, I had to go through the kitchen to reach the toilet, and there they were, scurrying squeaking, busy. I sent the Titch as an *avant-garde*, but they ignored her. Later I found them bomb-proof too.

The fishmonger, who now entered my family circle, was a joyful acquaintance. He was reaching retirement age, but he was not going to give up. Oh no, he loved his job. His straw hat was a memory of market days when he balanced baskets of fish on his head. He loved that as well. It was lovable. He had sixteen-year-old twin boys at a boarding-school somewhere in the country and was inordinately proud of them.

"We thought it was the change of life, the wife and I, but it was twins."

Guffaws of laughter. The wife, fat and happy in her glass box with the cash-register, nodding happily.

"One small fillet of cod? One fillet of cod it shall be."

The butcher was more stand-offish. Tall, blond, serious, possibly shy. He was engaged to be married next month.

The atmosphere in the street had changed. Impossible to say when the bright and easy talk about bombs and invasion turned into stoic anticipation. I saw no rush into houses or shelters at the sound of sirens; there was no cause for that yet. Most of us carried a nagging anxiety: what was it going to be like to be bombed? Would one be able to take it? How would one behave?

Once the Blitz started, one learned fast. The Germans came over punctually as darkness fell. Their regularity helped. One learned to recognize aircraft noises and their distance, to differentiate between the various types of bomb.

"If you hear a bomb whistling, it's not going to hit you. The one that's going to hit you, you won't hear," you were told. You lived through your ears. You learned that bombs straight overhead did not automatically kill you and deduced that no bomb would kill you, you led a charmed life. You still thought in terms of life or death, and never about the terrifying grey area in between. That knowledge came later. You always ducked, hunched your shoulders and ducked. In the middle of the room, to no purpose whatsoever, you ducked. You learned fast that ack-ack shell fragments would do a lot of damage. The searchlights you could watch as long as their long stabbing fingers pointed somewhere else. If they were lighting up the sky above, you could pray.

Hiding under the bedcovers with Titch during a raid did not work out, for my bed stood near the window. I could have moved it, I did not. We dashed towards the inner wall when bombs fell near by.

The Blitz, an experience shared by many, was lived through in individual ways. You were not harassed by regulations; you could choose where you wished to be bombed.

There was a steadily increasing pulling-together of all those who had decided to stay and see it through, not confined to friends, relatives or district. We were all in this together; everyone cared for everyone. The English people, so hard-put to wear a smile on their sleeves, now wore brotherhood on them, their courage high, their diffidence gone. I saw no panic, no hysteria, few tears – confusion at times at the sight of an unexploded bomb. There were many, many unsung heroes.

The Blitz was terrifying. To live through it with the people of London was a privilege. You saw the spirit win, you witnessed the brotherhood of man.

Eddie wrote that it was a question of a week, ten days at most, till he would be back. "See you soon. How is the flat?" I could feel his longing to sit at the kitchen table, a cup of coffee in front of him. Home! One week of bombs? Difficult to think "Thy will be done."

I rang Nick Serge. He invited me to dinner at the Ritz. I found it disagreeable to leave the house at the start of an air-raid and travel by bus with all that activity overhead. To sit in the brightly-lit, elegant dining-room at the Ritz was eerie. Great chunks of London were burning, people were being killed and maimed, while I chose *hors d'oeuvres*. Nothing would have changed had I not eaten there. The Ritz also could be bombed – they had bombed Buckingham Palace two days running.

Nick was helpful, friendly and tired. Everyone was tired. He would be delighted to meet Eddie. There was every chance of a job. Would I let him know when Eddie was back, bring them together?

Papa Schiff said the baby was holding its own. Quite a few of his patients had moved out during the last week or so – very sensible. An unspoken question mark after the 'sensible'. "See you in two weeks." We had finished with the injections. Two smacking kisses, a "God Bless".

I found a letter from Helen when I checked at the boarding-house. She wrote that she had no news from Feli; nor had she been able to establish Ursel's whereabouts. She had heard from Margit, who was in Lisbon, waiting for her papers from the Czech Embassy in London. There had been also a nearly illegible note from someone in Montpellier, who said that he· had taken a job as a night-porter in a hotel, and the dog was well.

"Does he mean Tova? Did you have to leave Tova behind?"

I waited for the final telegram from Eddie and watched the fires of London burning. My eyes traced the criss-cross patterns of searchlights dividing the night sky; my ears gauged all sounds and made dictatorial decisions of their own. I went to bed, dashed semi-conscious towards the inner wall, went back to bed again. The puppy dashed with me: it was bomb-trained. At the beginning of the heavy bombardments one lived through fear each night, through exhilaration each morning – a small victory, another day had been won. As the bombardments continued, the fear again lost some of its edge; exhilaration was swallowed up by fatigue.

I made one attempt to escape the waiting, went to a cinema, got caught in a raid and had to spend the whole night there. Three days after that unpleasant event, the telegram came.

Eddie's train was due in at eight. The Luftwaffe arrived at seven-fifteen in large numbers. The anti-aircraft guns swung into action.

Everything that had to be done I had done twice over. I had cleaned and polished till every hole in the lino, every dent in the furniture, stood out sharp and clear. The napkin lay on the table, shining white; the breadboard and bread were in position, flowers, even a candle. Our dinner stood ready in the oven. In the brown coffee-pot the coffee was prepared. I had lit an open fire.

I went downstairs to get myself one step nearer to Eddie's arrival. Bombs were exploding in a wide arc around me; shrapnel was click-clicking on the pavements; searchlights were sweeping the sky. I tried to pass the time by guessing the distance of the bombs by their noise. The street was empty, but occasionally a car came down, picking its way through the dark.

I thought how much of my time had been spent waiting during the last few months, from the waiting in Grau d'Agde onwards to waiting now, for Eddie to come home. I found myself suddenly grabbed and pulled indoors. My landlady and her husband had come to fetch me in.

"Don't you realize ... they're nearly overhead. Sit in the sitting-room if you like. You'll be able to see the taxi from there." They disappeared into their bathroom shelter.

I had not realized how much closer the raid had come. Waiting had extinguished time and place. Eddie should have been here at least half an hour ago. It had gone wrong. It had been bound to go wrong. I crept out again, stood in the doorway.

Perhaps destiny did not allow people like us to survive, people who had been gnawed at by fate! We might contaminate those who still believed. I was not likely to see Eddie again, of course not. Lead a normal life? How could I ever have hoped to return to a normal life? The whole misery I had so carefully locked away broke out over me. I felt like bashing my brains out against the front door. I should have done so against the door of the church on the Montparnasse when all of this first started, when Hitler walked into Austria. I could not take it any longer. I had had enough of this war, this lousy, hellish war. I did not want to live it for one more second, not even for Thomas. He would have to go down with me. Enough!

I did not bash my brains out. I turned towards the door and began to cry, and that was how Eddie found me. I neither heard nor saw his taxi when at long last it did arrive.

His train had been stopped outside the station for over an hour while the raid was overhead. The delay had been quite reasonable, quite normal under the circumstances. A whole miracle of normality!

Eddie took me upstairs.

"How beautiful!" he said, when he opened the door to our flat. I saw with surprise that it was beautiful.

The fire had gone out. How much more sensible it would have been to keep that fire burning instead of going to pieces waiting in the street. The room was still warm. The little dachshund was running around in joyful circles.

I lit the gas under the lidless brown coffee-jug. I lit the stove to warm our supper.

How beautiful!

8

Within a week of Eddie's home-coming we changed flats. The garden flat had become available. A garden flat increased your chances of retaining your windows and reduced fire-risks.

Our new flat was a mirror-image of the former one. The bath was painted green instead of blue; the geyser was slightly more forthcoming; the mice moved with us.

We had been busy during that first week. Eddie had met Nicky Serge after office hours, and the two men had got on well with each other. Technical details had flowed over me in a mixture of Czech, Polish and German. Nicky did need an engineer: he wanted to increase production and open up in Canada, and he might want to send Eddie over. He would give him a ring in a day or two. We hardly dared look at each other when we left. Dreams! Handle with care!

At the weekend our landlady announced that they could not stand the bombing any more: she and her husband were going to move out of London. The oldest tenant, Mrs Green, would take charge of the house and move down into their flat. The oldest tenant was an unpleasant woman who unsuccessfully tried to cope with a job during the day, a drunken husband in the evening, the Blitz during the night.

The departure of our hosts introduced the problem of the telephone. During the day there would be no one to answer it unless either Eddie or I stayed at home. During the evening Mrs Green was at home and would answer it, but we could not be sure that she would pass on a message. We were anxiously waiting for Nicky Serge's call.

Not the telephone but the post was good to us. On one of my occasional calls to the boarding-house I found a letter from

Helen and a parcel with many official stamps. In the parcel was my camera. I had not thought that I would ever see it again.

The letter contained no news of Feli or Ursel. Were we all right? Could I do with twenty pounds, enclosed herewith?

We went out and equipped Eddie for civilian life. There was enough money left to indulge in a maternity dress for me – none too soon, the efficiency of safety-pins is limited. Steffi's clothes I had had to abandon entirely; my own showed signs of strain.

Pleased with our acquisitions, we rushed back home to the telephone. I couldn't hear the happy 'yep-yep' of our little dachshund when we entered the house. I could not hear the patter of paws on lino when we put the key in the door. At first we could not even see the Titch. She was lying stiff and unconscious in a corner of the room.

She looked dead. Eddie discovered that she was breathing and scooped her up.

"A fit," he said. "I'll try and bring her round."

After the second attack we took her to the vet. Distemper of the brain – had she not been injected against distemper? No? Oh dear!

"She has one chance in a hundred," said the vet. "I would not advise you ..." The little golden-brown animal, which had been so warm and alive in my hands. Bright puppy eyes, many sorrowful folds on the forehead – and now one chance in a hundred?

We took the one chance and worked at it. We took it in turns to sleep for a couple of hours at a time. The incessant vigil brought no results; devotion did not win. After a week we took what was left of our puppy to the vet and had her put to sleep. She was not conscious when the needle went in.

She had been eight weeks old when I bought her; she was three and a half months old when she died. We buried her in the garden outside our window. All our unburied sorrows stood with us around her grave, nodding.

The telephone still had not rung.

The telephone did not ring; the bombs continued to fall; Eddie's demob papers arrived; notification of available jobs did not arrive from the Labour Exchange. Once again Eddie started to make ugly noises about growing cabbages in the country.

For several days now the gas had been cut off, bombs having damaged a main. We cooked on the open fire or went in relays to the Czech Club, one of us always guarding the phone. The street in which we lived had become unattractive: in every second house shattered windows were boarded up or covered with black material. It was easy to forget why we were putting up with all the danger and inconveniences. We did not forget.

What seemed to us like an eternity might seem like a couple of days to Nicky. I decided to ring him up, while Eddie was at the club.

"I'm alone in London, Eddie has had to go back to camp for a few days."

It is easy to lie, just not pleasant.

"Oh, fine, let's have dinner."

Eddie sat at the kitchen table, dressed in his uniform in order to safeguard the one precious suit, head in hand, saying that he did not enjoy sending me out into the streets in the middle of an air-raid; he had no real talent for the role of a pimp. His stupid remark stupidly lingered. Nick was his usual undemanding self. He had been to see Steffi and thought she was bored, Bernard more fussy than ever. He himself had had a lot of trouble at the factory.

"Apropos factory, I really must give Eddie a ring. When will he be back? In two days? Fine."

The return journey was terrifying. Anti-aircraft guns in Hyde Park were frantically busy, shooting straight into my back. I was cringing and twisting on my seat and ended up sitting on the floor of the cab, holding my handbag over my head.

"It's what you believe in that matters," the taxi-driver said as I tumbled shamefacedly out of the cab.

"What do you believe in?"

"If it's got my name on it, it'll find me."

Eddie was still at the kitchen table, arms on the table, head on his arms. He was not asleep.

Later we made coffee.

Still later we played rummy. The final stand-by. There

were mainly incendiary bombs that night. Eddie made the rounds with the stirrup-pump, accompanied by Mrs Green, whose husband lay snoring in drunken stupor.

The telephone-call came. Eddie was to meet the secretary of the company at Swiss Cottage tube station. I expected him to be away for the day, but he came back at lunchtime, looked frozen. He had stood for over two hours at the tube station, but no one had come.

"A misunderstanding," he said.

We swept the disappointment under the kitchen table and continued our telephone vigil. We stuck to the house like limpets, answering every telephone-call that came.

Papa Schiff was satisfied with my progress, looked at me with tired, loving eyes, no longer beamed, smiled a tired, loving smile.

"We'll have to decide sometime where you are going to have your child," he said.

Where I was going to have my child?

I had received Thomas's first fluttering greetings with joy. I nodded happily to him as his movements grew stronger. It was still the boy, between six and seven years old, that I was so happily nodding to. Suddenly I realized that Thomas would not be born aged six or seven, dressed in khaki-coloured shorts and an open yellow shirt. There was a gap between my dream and the approaching realities.

I had handled plenty of babies in the Viennese hospital where I had worked, but how did one prepare for the arrival of one? I needed information. A book would have to do.

The book threw me. It stated that everything a baby needed should be ready for it at the start of the seventh month. There were long lists of items grouped together under the name of 'layette' – minimum layettes and maximum layettes.

The seventh month was not far away, but there was not a single basic nappy in sight. The smallest bird was better prepared for its young than I was. I was unfit to be a mother, irresponsible.

I gave up the struggle to clean the flat without water – a water-main had been hit, and to cook without water or gas. I did not go shopping or visit the Czech Club – undamaged so far. I sat and grieved.

"I'll take you to the Czech Red Cross," Eddie said, after watching me for two days.

"What can the Czech Red Cross do?"

"We'll see what it can do, won't we."

"What about the telephone."

"To hell with the telephone."

We travelled on the top of a bus through bomb-damaged London to a sort of warehouse with long counters and cold concrete flooring. Huddled-up figures stood behind counters and shelves, which reached to the ceiling.

"Have you by any chance any baby clothes? Please."

The huddled-up figures straightened, became animated, hurried in various directions.

"Nothing very elaborate," they said sadly and shook their heads, "but good solid stuff ..." and they brightened up again. "Easy to launder, you'll see. Pink edging or blue edging? Or white, to be on the safe side? Blue? Yes, of course."

The shawls were all second-hand – pity, wasn't it? But then shawls did not get used all that much, did they? They had recently received some hand-knitted matinée jackets; would I like one of those? I looked at the shelves: they seemed to be stacked high with love.

We came home much richer than when we left. There was a 'layette'; Eddie had received a 'demob' suit, and I a coat, which buttoned up in front now and would do so in weeks to come. More than that, we had seen an international network of care in action.

9

The telephone-call, when it came, was a surprise.

Dashing to the phone whenever it did ring during the day had become a habit. I took most calls – Eddie's much improved English was inclined to let him down on the line. Nicky sounded positive and efficient. Could Eddie make his own way out to the factory? No one had time to meet him halfway. Day after tomorrow at ten; ask for Mr Stevenson. Mr Stevenson would take him round. Report back. Nick spelled out the address and gave me directions on how to get to the factory; I took the address down, and the directions floated away on waves of excitement. A map; we needed a map. We rushed to the post office. No map; suspicous glances; aliens were not allowed to own maps.

You overcome real problems and get defeated by pinpricks. Might the boffin help, lend us a map, buy one for us, trace Eddie's route for him?

The boffin was limping badly when I went to see him. A shell-splinter had had to be taken out of his leg some time ago; the wound was not healing properly; he did not give it a chance to do so; he acted as an air-raid warden. Of course he would get a map for us. Best to let him have it back when we had finished with it.

We pored all evening over the map, made a tracing of the route and rehearsed phrases in case Eddie got lost and had to ask the way.

He left very early, and it was late when he came back. He walked differently. He held his head differently.

He had reported back to the office from the factory. In Czech. There was much that he would be able to contribute. He was to return next day, possibly the day after, draw up plans. At the end of the week he was offered the job on a month's trial.

Some people discover new continents. Lesser ones discover a way back from the rubbish-heap, and to them it feels as if they also had discovered a new continent.

We belonged to the lesser ones.

One night, when we had reached the fairly desperate card-playing stage in our 'how to cope with air-raids' routine, there came the dreaded moment of unholy silence. Then the thin, barely audible whistle. Eddie shouted: "Bathroom!" but it was already too late. The house swayed, seemed to lean towards the street, rocked back towards the garden, tottered ... We waited for its imminent collapse – it stood. We waited for the outside wall to crumble and disappear – the window exploded inwards, covering us with glass – the wall did not crumble. We waited for our world to end – nothing more happened. We were shaken but alive, covered with small cuts but otherwise unhurt. We dashed downstairs. Mr and Mrs Green emerged from the bathroom. We all went into the street without even noticing that the house-door had been blown off. We were promptly chased back into the house – rescue-workers needed all the space they could get between glass, bricks, rooftiles. A warden came in, checked that the house was safe and did not have to be evacuated at once. An ambulance-worker helped brush glass out of our hair, faces, clothes, daubed us with antiseptic. Best thing we could do would be to start sweeping up the glass. We started sweeping up the glass. Mr Green had a bottle of whisky and gave us all a nip. Mrs Green said that we would have to look for other accommodation: she did not want the responsibility for anyone in the house any longer. And she herself? She did not know – the tube shelter, maybe.

Eddie left early for his job.

"I'll try to get back early, before the raids start. Don't worry if you can't get accommodation for the night, Mrs Green can't put us out on the street."

I left soon after Eddie to see how my shopping street had fared.

It was a shambles. The damage was arbitrary, inexplicable, as if the bomb-blast had run amok, battering corners in here, pushing windows out there. The house above the butcher's shop was down. There were other people in the street, trying to find out what had happened to their shopkeeper friends.

Their steps clatter-clatter sharply on the pavement. Their faces are masks with agonized eyes. I know most of them. Lately we have occasionally exchanged a few words.

"Terrible night, wasn't it ... did you get any sleep?"

Today we exchange no words, do not even look at each other. We each follow our chosen path.

My friend at the greengrocer's is sweeping glass off the pavement with slow, heavy movements. The broom swirls; her large pale face is covered in dust; her tears carve vertical lines into it, giving it the appearance of a clown's face. The blast has torn away the front wall of the house above; floors hang crazily in mid-air. No one has been hurt: they were all in the shelter; so was she, but her flat has gone.

"What are you going to do, where are you going to live?"

She shrugs her shoulders; she does not know; her sister might take her in. She had little before, now she has less.

The boffin is not in his shop. Window and door have been blown in, but the door to the workshop is all right; it is locked; there is a notice pinned to it: "Back tomorrow". Further down the road the bakery is already shuttered up. The notice pinned up on the board says "No bread today".

"They're all right," says a woman, staring at the same notice. "They hadn't started baking, there was no one in."

Samuel stands at the counter in his shop. The shelves behind him are empty apart from the photo, which is lying there flat and crumpled. Samuel has made no attempt to clear up. He has simply swept a path in a straight line from the missing door across to the counter. He seems temporarily deranged, standing there in his over-all in the cold, saying:

"What can I get you?"

There is a vacant look in his eyes. Through the open door one can see a candle burning in the stockroom; there is a candle on the counter in front of him. I am completely taken aback by his question.

"A tin of pea-soup, please."

Samuel disappears into the stockroom, comes back with the tin, ignores the many tins of soup strewn around on the floor.

"I can't let my customers down, you see," he tells me in a confidential tone and shakes his head. "Can't let them down."

Does he really think that he will be able to cut little bits of paper out of rationbooks with those trembling hands?

His shop is wide open to wind and rain, no windows, no door, the ceiling half down, no customers yet, apart from me. Samuel's mind is closed. He holds on to his one security, standing behind the counter, serving. I ask him:

"Is your daughter coming to help you? Your nephew? Can I help clear up? Are you not going to board up the shop?"

"I can't let my customers down," repeats Samuel, smiles and looks insane. It is early yet, perhaps somebody will come and look after him; he has looked after many people in the past.

"I'll come back in the afternoon, see how you are getting on." I doubt that he has heard me.

On the opposite side of the road I can see the fishmonger and his wife searching through the rubble of their shop for salvage. No straw hat, no blue-striped apron. No smile.

"This is it," he says, "this is the end of it."

He is going to move out of London, nearer to the twins. His wife looks at me, her eyes dry and full of agony for her man. How do these people keep their eyes dry?

At the butcher's shop, activities are frantic. I can see the boffin, the greengrocer, other people from the street; they are silently passing rubble along from hand to hand. Occasionally everything stops, everyone listening intently.

"The butcher had a flat in the basement," someone whispers to me. "He was giving a pre-wedding party."

Several people are trapped, but voices have been heard. The boffin is limping towards me.

"We've only just been able to cut off their electricity," he says despairingly. "He used electric fires in his flat."

There is nothing I can do in my street at this moment. I go away. I must try to find a room for Eddie and myself for the night. It is very difficult to find anything, too many houses have been bombed, too many landladies have moved away. Eddie insists that we must stay within reach of the club, and I would not know where to start looking outside the district – a district becomes like a village after a while. It seems to me that

I have walked for many hours when I stand outside a small boarding-house, and a warm, melodious voice says:

"Will it be for tonight that you'll be wanting a bed?"

No double room, but two small single rooms are available, with breakfast and dinner. "Had you better come in, sit yourself down and have a hot cup of tea?" It is a solid young woman who has invited me in. She has dark hair and large blue eyes. Her name is Mary, and she comes from Dublin.

My friend the greengrocer's assistant has gone when I go back to the street, but her boss is in the shop. Some people from the neighbourhood have taken her in for the afternoon and night, he says. The people from the butcher's flat have been brought out. There had been eight in all: four have been brought out alive; one more died on the way to hospital.

Samuel is still standing behind his counter. A tide of relatives and friends are cleaning up around him, rearranging shelves, boarding-up windows and door. Samuel waves them aside majestically whenever they come too near him.

"Make room for the customers. Get out of the way. I've to serve."

Nobody takes any notice of his commands.

The boffin is sitting in his little workshop. He still has his overcoat on; his hands are rammed in his coat-pockets; he is staring straight in front of him.

"The electric fire," he whispers, "he was buried on top of the electric fire."

I had not realized that the blond butcher had been his friend. His friend is dead. I stay with the boffin till four, till I must go back to the flat. Would he like to come with me, spend the evening with us? He is going back on duty at six.

A new dimension has been added to one's fears, the grey area. Between black and white, between life and death — survival can become the real horror.

10

To be once again without a kitchen seemed a retrograde step to me, but Eddie settled in to the new arrangements with enthusiasm. I would no longer be alone during the day. He could devote himself body and soul to his job. I had married a company before; I was living with a factory now. My close contacts were Mary and a bombed-out cat.

The owners of the small boarding-house were conspicuous by their absence, and Mary, the maid, by her presence. She was everywhere at the same time. Mary sang while she worked, sad Irish ballads that floated through the house. While her hands, holding duster or polishing cloths, flew swiftly over the various surfaces, her voice brought forth the slow waltz rhythm of 'Somewhere a voice is calling', 'Mother Machree' and others, an impressive feat. 'The Mountains of Mourne' was her favourite song, her longing for them not influenced by the fact that they were near Belfast and she came from Dublin.

As soon as the sirens went, Mary would disappear into her room, then re-appear wearing a small white handkerchief on top of her dark curly hair. The handkerchief had been blessed by the priest. It would safeguard her. "Holy Mother of God preserve us" and the sign of the cross acknowledged the thud of bombs. Between crossing herself and murmuring incantations, Mary carried on with her work.

I had nothing to do, and the days were long. I took it upon myself to clean our two little rooms, for Mary had plenty to do. I would be better occupied, she stated, "a-knitting for the babe". I had never knitted before, though crocheting had been forced on me as a girl. Mary undoubtedly had sucked in the art of knitting with her mother's milk. I obediently went out and bought white wool and knitting-needles. I found it a very irritating occupation.

"Holy Mother of God, you make a mess of it, and no mistake," said Mary.

I did make a mess of it, and no mistake. I produced something which looked like a short, grubby bit of bandage.

"It's ashamed of yourself you should be!"

I was. I had the feeling that Thomas was watching me from a long way away, helpless with laughter. The baby inside me might have appreciated the results of my efforts, had there been any. I wondered why the two had split in my mind: Thomas, so familiar, moving out of reach; the baby, an unknown entity, a stranger. Would they become one again at some future moment?

The cat was prettily marked in black and white and used to belong to a film-actress. When the young actress, bombed out, had moved away, the cat had made her home under the debris of her former house and had given birth to dead kittens there. She was slowly being lured away from her home by Mary, who had made a place for her near the boiler in the scullery.

"Sweet Jesus, the poor wee crayture ..."

Outside my window was an attempt at a balcony which ended one foot after it began: one day the cat appeared on the ledge of the balcony rail. I gave her some milk. She returned. She came in the morning in time for breakfast, in the afternoon in time for tea (a gift from Mary).

"You'll not be saying no to a nice cup of tea, I'm thinking."

Sometimes the cat let me stroke her.

One evening Eddie came home from work smiling as if he had been travelling by winged chariot instead of by tube.

"I've heard of a dog going spare," he said.

"When?" I asked him.

"When what?"

"When did you arrange for it to come?"

It was not as easy as that. The young owner had just received his call-up papers and wanted to be sure he could have the dog back, if he managed to survive the war, if the dog was still alive then. Eddie explained it all ponderously.

"You must be quite sure."

I was quite sure. I knew very well what the owner of the dog felt.

I was unprepared for the sight that faced me two days later when I answered a hesitant knock and opened the door. A boy stood outside, a tall, blond boy. He looked so very young, too young for war. He had large blue eyes. Every freckle stood out separately on his pale face. He did not say one word. His lips were quivering, and he pressed them together as hard as he could, while big tears ran out of his eyes.

In a country where tears are so rare, where jokes are shields to hide emotions from prying eyes, naked grief on so young a face is devastating.

The boy handed me the lead with a large brown curly-haired dog at its end. Worm-powder, flea-powder, shampoo, boracic eye-lotion, a brush, a steel comb, a rubber bone, a ball – one by one, he fetched all these things out of various pockets of his uniform with long-fingered boyish hands that shook. Still without saying a word, he saluted, turned on his heels and ran down the stairs. He never told me the name of the dog.

I closed the door. The dog howled. I howled.

We called the dog 'Pieter Brown'. Pieter Brown decided to accept us. Reluctantly at first, whole-heartedly later. I lost my bad conscience about Tova. She and Pieter Brown had nothing in common except four paws. Alsatians adapt themselves to their masters; Pieter Brown adapted me to himself.

No more sauntering along anywhere during the day. Wherever we went, we went at the double. If I did not watch out, we went at the double to Hyde Park.

At my next monthly visit, Papa Schiff said it was about time I thought of my baby. I told him I had thought of little else during the past months.

"So," he said, folding his hands across his stomach and looking at me like an owl, "Where are you going to wash the nappies then? Where are you going to put the cot, or the pram? Is our baby going to be kept awake every night by bombs? Where," he leaned forward and bored holes into me with his big dark eyes, "where are you going to permit me to deliver it?"

"There, there," he said later, holding six feet of very pregnant crying female in his arms, "I know, it's difficult without a mum."

In theory I had three alternatives. The hospital in which Papa Schiff worked; a nursing-home outside London in Beaconsfield, which he knew and was willing to attend; a nursing-home in Hendon. 'At home' was out, even if we did find a decent home.

"I want a fully equipped operating-theatre to be available. I'm sure we won't need it, but it must be there."

Beaconsfield! More than half an hour away by train or car. How would I know in time that the baby was coming?

"You'll notice," said Papa Schiff. "I promise you, you will not miss the arrival of your child. Get yourself a flat first. Look somewhere in the north of London – Barnet, that sort of district. They have not been so heavily bombed – I want to see you in a fortnight," he added.

So dreaming about Thomas had to stop for a while; the layette alone was not enough. I set off next day.

Barnet was already full. Other people had discovered its advantages. An agent sent me to Finchley. There was a ground-floor flat available in a block of flats: two bedrooms, a sitting-room, minute dining-room, kitchen, bath. Too good to be true, bound to be bombed before we got there.

"First of January," said the agent.

I implored him to make it 31st December. I explained that I was superstitious: whatever I did on the first of the year I would continue doing throughout the year. I had visions of moving from place to place all through 1941, as I had done in 1940. He looked at me as if I were round the bend. He relented.

"All right, the 31st."

The flat bore the imprint of the people who had chosen it and furnished it. From cradle to marriage to the flat in one straight line – even destiny tamed by tradition? Did we have the right to intrude? Would our presence in it taint the place with insecurity and upheaval? Bring the Luftwaffe down on it?

I reported progress to Papa Schiff. "Good, good," he nodded. "Fine. And now: nursing-home or hospital? "Good girl," he added unexpectedly.

I took my camera and sold it to a shop in Bond Street. I wanted to make as sure as I could of avoiding hospital, regimentation, *roskas*, being a number without the right of decision. But that camera had been a friend.

"Have a look at least at Beaconsfield. Let me deliver you somewhere where it will be peaceful for you and the baby." Papa Schiff's dark eyes had been pleading with me on my behalf, had made me feel like melting wax. I travelled out to Beaconsfield and found the nursing-home.

I have many hackles. 'Matron' made all of them rise. She was stiff, starched, in a hurry and very superior. They would find it very difficult to fit me in – verrry. It was not a good date for them, not at all. She really couldn't guarantee anything.

Her voice implied that it was foolish and improvident to want to give birth to a child without booking months ahead and that it only served me right if now I had to suffer the consequences of my foolishness and improvidence. The matron was thin, past middle-age, I disliked her immensely. Her sharp little eyes tore my shabby blue coat to shreds. I resented that. The coat had been lovingly given to me. Perhaps she just disliked mothers. So many matrons, and teachers, do.

The nursing-home in Hendon was next. When I finally did find it, it was a surprise. It looked like an ordinary house, the walls inside not even painted white. The basement had been turned into an operating-theatre.

They were reluctantly willing to accept me. If it had to be. Because Dr Schiff had recommended me. They were short of staff – staff had moved out of London. The responsibility!

"You must understand, a mother-to-be needs a lot of attention. We do not really like to take maternity cases."

In general, so it seemed to me, the occupants of prams were treated like royalty, while the producers of future pram-occupants carried the Victorian stigma of 'sin'.

Papa Schiff declared himself satisfied.

"If there is any change," his eyes boring holes into me again, "any difference at all in your condition, ring me at once. At once! Day or night. I don't mind if it is a false alarm, leave the judgement of that to me. I can be with you within the hour. See you in the New Year."

I wondered what was still worrying him. I did not ask.

On Saturday afternoon Eddie and I went to the flat together. I could see from his eyes that to him too our aspiration to occupy that simple little flat seemed like reaching for the moon. It was too normal. Its surroundings were too normal. We were refugees; we did not belong here. We belonged to places like the one-room flat where suffering humanity had left a warmth and a welcome behind, places which demanded nothing. They made us feel safe.

Places not suitable for a child.

11

On an early return-trip to the new district, one of many to arrange for lifelines such as gas, electricity, water, coal, registrations of all kinds, I discovered the Common and became a regular visitor.

Finchley Common. People say that a winter landscape is barren, but it is not. It is desolate, and it is beautiful. A bare landscape – but not barren, beautiful in its truth, waiting to live again, bring forth once more, explode with the miracle of life in its innumerable forms.

Finchley Common – a piece of wasteland, neglected ground, rough and wild, untrammelled by flowerbeds and tidy paths, a miniscule plot in this world and holding all of its magic, a dot between concrete and bricks. Wind and rain, fog at times, closing down distance, springing the next bush at you, a surprise encounter. I felt at peace on the Common. I felt safe under the wintry sky. Like the last of the fallen leaves, my thoughts flew free in the wind.

Thomas! Close to me now and saying 'Goodbye'. Closer than he had been for the last disjointed months and telling me that he now had to go. I could see him in my mind as clearly as I had seen him that first time, one far-away evening in Paris, feel him as near as I had felt him on the *Northmoor*. "It will be all right." I had held on to him, had lived within him as much as he had lived within me. He was sailing away on a cloud, leaving me to grow alone into reality. And if his spirit was to enter the body of the unborn child, would he ever again be mine as much as he had been? No human being belongs to another. We are caretakers only, allowed to serve, to give, to receive, never to own.

Thomas. By the time that he was due to be born, I would

have known of him for sixteen months – and been a refugee for three years less one month. A short time and an eternity.

Many people walked with me across Finchley Common, headed by Ursel, still carrying 'Antoinette'. Only God knows how much I loved them then, how much I love them still. The 'sparrows', so young, so vulnerable and so hurt. Sven, getting drunk, flailing about to escape from the mire which threatened to suck him under. Monsieur Louis, who had killed his canaries.

Toni, and his abominable cat's skin; the army doctor with the tired eyes; Eliane of the velvety dark ones; even the colonel's wife holding on to rank; the doctor, who sobbed because he could not find his prunes in the dirt; Margit and Hedi; the woman who threw her child overboard; the young Polish pilots with their empty hands; Renée.

Grains of sand, swept under, swept to distant shores. Fellow-refugees, comrades, I greet them, the ones I knew and the ones I shall never know.

I realized, during my walks through wind and rain, that soon now I would return to the confines of a personal life, leave the wider plane of multiple hope and suffering, devote myself to the care of those who were entrusted to my care or within its reach. Hide behind my aspidistra and net curtains, glance up occasionally from behind my papers? I was not going to have an aspidistra, or net curtains; this was not going to be the aim of the struggle to put life together again.

I was not going to forget, and I have not forgotten.

When I came to my little shopping street for the last time, the bomb-scars stood out starkly, but life within the buildings was recovering.

The greengrocer was busy in the remnants of his existing shop; soon he would have to leave it, the house above was not safe. He was going to take over the fishmonger's former premises, once they had been made usable. My friend the four-square woman in sack-like garments, with the large pale face, was away staying with her sister for a short Christmas holiday. Oh yes, she was coming back; she had found a furnished room in the neighbourhood. The bakery was still boarded up, but a notice on the door said: 'Business as usual'.

Samuel's shop was in full swing, three notices of 'Business as usual' informing you that this was so, one on each boarded-up window, one on the door. Samuel did nothing by halves.

The boffin's leg had healed. His grief had not. He looked thin, drawn, the intense dark eyes dark-ringed. What about taking one of his freshly repaired radios with us to the new flat? As a Christmas present? We would come back and buy one. Soon. Would he come and visit us in the new flat? Of course he would. Good-bye and God Bless. He would not come and visit us – he knew it, and we knew it.

My little street, scarred but alive once more. Only the young blond butcher and his four friends had 'bought the wrong ticket' and were gone.

On our last night at the boarding-house, we did not feel all that bright.

I would miss Mary, 'The Mountains of Mourne', the 'Smiling Irish Eyes' and 'Rose of Tralee'. At times she had reminded me of Ursel, warm-hearted and practical, courageous and devoted. I left some liver behind for the cat, as a New Year's gift. She now slept in the scullery, but the night before, when Hitler tried to set London alight and largely succeeded, she had become quite frantic in her efforts to reach her hidey-hole under the bombed house. I was preparing for my dream to come true, but it meant leaving the few people I cared for in London behind.

We left at about two in the afternoon. Eddie carried our cases and the box with the baby's layette. I had the typewriter, the lodencape and a bag of groceries, including a chicken I had bought as a special treat for New Year's Eve. I had Pieter on the lead. It was a cumbersome exodus.

We must have presented a sorry picture, stumbling towards our new abode. We ought to have been jubilant and were not. The cases, boxes and bags were heavy, our invisible luggage heavier.

The little flat was cold. The coal had not come, but the lady next door loaned us a scuttle of hers. We lit a fire in the sitting-room; the bedrooms had built-in gasfires – those we did not light; we were not yet ready to take possession of the bedrooms. I had difficulty in making up my mind to unpack and hang clothes in the empty wardrobe. I did not wish to disturb anything. The room which was to be the nursery was nice and bright; it had light yellow wallpaper and curtains with flowers on a light yellow background. It looked out into the garden. I went in and out of the room several times; it had a single bed, no cot. I would have to get a cot. I decided not to unpack the layette but leave the clothes in the box, put the box in the wardrobe in our bedroom. Keep the child close.

The electricity had not been connected, so Eddie went out to get candles. Later I put the chicken on to roast. The sitting-room was getting warm. It had a settee and an easy chair – a full-sized easy chair, like the one on the ship. well-worn, lovable. The pieces of furniture began to grow towards us. It was very still. The window of the sitting-room looked on to the lawn in front of the Court, green, even now. Coffee? We could make coffee!

The doorbell rang – very surprising, we had not realized that we had a doorbell. A young woman and an ARP warden stood outside. Could they have our names, some details?

"Do come in."

They came in and stood, slightly embarrassed, in the sitting-room, lit up by the fire and one candle. Would Eddie be able to take part in the fire-watching rota? Oh good. Of course he would always be able to ask for a stand-in if ... They were very shy. How long had we been in England?

"You understand, we are only taking down these details for official use."

What was our former address? What were the addresses of our next of kin, whom we wanted informed in case of ...

They insisted that there must be someone, whose address we knew, whom we wished informed. Their embarrassment made them stubborn.

It took us a long time before we could think of anyone whose address we might give. Nick in Mayfair, Steffi in Walton-on-Thames. The two visitors left, drained by the difficulty of their task. We saw them out, returned, sat down. I forgot about the chicken, remembered it only when I could smell it burning.

The burned chicken was a relief, a harmless direction for pent-up emotion. You could fuss about it, laugh about it, be busy. Parts of it were still eatable.

We came to again. The room was warm and comfortable,

the flames of the open fire soothing. We had survived 1940. We had been very lucky. It seemed an achievement to have survived 1940! We were together, the three of us. Eddie had work; we were earning our living. One says it lightly, but it is a basis for self-respect. For the time being, at least, we had a home. With a cooker. With a double bed. The cot was to come. I had not, not at all, forgotten how beautiful and how impossible a dream that had seemed to me. Soon the baby would be born, a new life, embodiment of hope.

For a moment we felt as if mountains had been moved, miracles achieved. We never left the sitting-room that night. We saw the New Year in, and our love brought close to us, into the room, our families, whose whereabouts we no longer knew. They were with us. They were in us.

Eddie slept in the easy chair; I slept on the settee, and Pieter Brown stretched out in front of the fire. The sitting-room had become familiar; the rest of the flat was unknown territory. Tomorrow was another day.

Tomorrow was the first day of a brand new year. Would I have reached that year, I wondered, without the help of Thomas?

Postscript

The baby was born in February.

Air-raids had started up again. It was difficult to find a taxi. The journey, through unknown side streets in the dark to avoid unexploded bombs, took long.

Matron was kind: she let Eddie stay with me the night. But he had long gone to work, and we were halfway through the next day before I heard Papa Schiff say:

"It's a boy! It's a lovely baby boy" and saw his beaming face close above mine. "It's a lovely baby boy," he repeated. "He's all right. You're all right. Everything is all right."

"Eight and a half pounds," stated a matter-of-fact voice in the background, and I wondered how something which had been as big as the sky above me for months could weigh just eight and a half pounds.

We named the child after his grandfather, the station-master in Brno.